W9-DFY-920

 UIC The University of Illinois
at Chicago

The original edition was based on work supported by the National Science Foundation under grant No. MDR 9050226 and the University of Illinois at Chicago. Any opinions, findings, and conclusions or recommendations expressed in this publication are those of the author(s) and do not necessarily reflect the views of the granting agencies.

LETTER HOME

Applications: An Assessment Unit

Date: _____

Dear Family Member:

So far this year, students have had many opportunities to complete laboratory experiments. In this unit, students complete a lab to assess their abilities to collect and analyze data while studying the life spans of people, animals, and soap bubbles.

Several other assessments are also included in this unit. Students read an Adventure Book about Florence Kelley, a social reformer who collected data on child labor. They write a report that displays and analyzes data she collected. They also take a paper-and-pencil test on skills and concepts learned since the beginning of the school year. At the end of the unit, students will add activities from this unit to their portfolios. They will review their portfolios comparing newly completed activities to old in order to show their growth in mathematics.

Students play a game to practice multiplying decimals.

As we work through this unit, you can help your child by doing the following activities at home:

- Ask your child to tell you about the Adventure Book.

- Play the game *Three in a Row* with your child after it has been played in school.

- Help your child practice the multiplication and division facts using the *Triangle Flash Cards.* Your child's fluency with these facts will be assessed as part of this unit.

Thank you for your support.

Sincerely,

_____

UNIT OUTLINE

Applications: An Assessment Unit

Pacing Suggestions

This unit will take 9 to 14 days to complete. It includes a variety of review and assessment activities that provide opportunities for teachers to assess individual growth in mathematics as students continue learning while applying concepts and skills in new contexts.

- Lessons 2 and 7 are optional lessons. Lesson 2 *Three in a Row* is a challenging game that practices estimation with decimals. Lesson 7 *Review Problems* is a set of word problems that reviews skills and concepts from the first seven units. These problems can be assigned for homework. Lesson 7 is also appropriate for use by a substitute teacher.

- Lesson 3 *Florence Kelley* is an Adventure Book story that provides a strong connection both to language arts and social studies. It sets the stage for the open-response assessment problem in Lesson 4 *Florence Kelley's Report*. Allow two days for Lesson 4 if you plan to give students the opportunity to revise their responses. Alternatively, you can use language arts time for students to read the story or write and revise their responses.

- Lesson 5 *Life Spans* and Lesson 6 *Comparing Lives of Animals and Soap Bubbles* provide connections to science. Students can collect the data for the lab in Lesson 6 during science time.

Components Key: SG = Student Guide, DAB = Discovery Assignment Book, AB = Adventure Book, URG = Unit Resource Guide, and DPP = Daily Practice and Problems

	Sessions	Description	Supplies
LESSON 1 **Experiment Review** SG page 270 DAB pages 135–136 URG pages 21–29 DPP A–B	1	**ACTIVITY:** Students review experiments completed in the last seven units in preparation for the assessment lab in this unit.	
LESSON 2	*– OPTIONAL LESSON – ENRICHMENT MATERIAL –*		
Three in a Row DAB pages 137–139 URG pages 30–33	1	**OPTIONAL GAME:** Students play a game which involves estimating products of decimals.	• game markers or tokens • calculators
LESSON 3 **Florence Kelley** AB pages 47–60 SG pages 271–272 URG pages 34–43 DPP C–D	1	**ADVENTURE BOOK:** Students learn about the life of Florence Kelley, who helped reduce child labor in Chicago around 1900. They use data she collected to make predictions.	• calculators

	Sessions	Description	Supplies
LESSON 4 **Florence Kelley's Report** URG pages 44–57 DPP E–F	1–2	**ASSESSMENT ACTIVITY:** Students use the Adventure Book in Lesson 3 to demonstrate their abilities to graph and analyze data. They describe their conclusions in writing. **ASSESSMENT PAGE:** *Florence Kelley's Report*, Unit Resource Guide, page 56.	• calculators
LESSON 5 **Life Spans** SG pages 273–275 DAB page 141 URG pages 58–68 DPP G–H	1–2	**ACTIVITY:** Students compare human life span data from 1858 to life span data from 1997. They organize and graph the data, scaling the vertical axis using percents.	• calculators
LESSON 6 **Comparing Lives of Animals and Soap Bubbles** SG pages 276–279 DAB page 143 URG pages 69–79 DPP I–N	3	**ASSESSMENT LAB:** Students collect data about the life spans of soap bubbles. This data is compared to the life spans of animals. Students scale the vertical axis using percents.	• bubble solution • bubble wands • stopwatches • calculators • paper towels
LESSON 7 **Review Problems** SG pages 280–281 URG pages 80–83	1	*– OPTIONAL LESSON – REVIEW MATERIAL –* **OPTIONAL ACTIVITY:** Students solve word problems using ratios, decimals, and percents.	• centiwheels • rulers • calculators
LESSON 8 **Midyear Test** URG pages 84–93 DPP O–P	1–2	**ASSESSMENT ACTIVITY:** Students take a short item test assessing skills and concepts learned in Units 2–8. **ASSESSMENT PAGES:** *Midyear Test*, Unit Resource Guide, pages 87–91.	• rulers • protractors • calculators

	Sessions	Description	Supplies

LESSON 9

Portfolio Review

SG   pages 282–283

URG   pages 94–99

DPP   Q–R

Sessions: 1

Description: **ASSESSMENT ACTIVITY:** Students update and review their portfolios.

Supplies:
- collection folder
- portfolio folder

CONNECTIONS

A current list of connections is available at www.kendallhunt.com.

Literature

Suggested Titles

- Appelhoff, Mary, Mary Frances Fenton, and Barbara Loss Harris. *Worms Eat Our Garbage.* Flower Press, Kalamazoo, MI, 1993.
- Cole, Joanna. *The Magic School Bus: Lost in Space.* Scholastic, New York, 1990.
- Schwartz, David M. *If You Made a Million.* Scholastic, New York, 1989.
- The EarthWorks Group. *50 Simple Things Kids Can Do to Save the Earth.* Andrews and McMeel, Kansas City, MO, 1999.
- Wilder, Laura Ingalls. *Little House in the Big Woods.* HarperCollins, New York, 2001.

Software

- *Fraction Attraction* develops understanding of fractions using fraction bars, pie charts, hundreds blocks, and other materials.
- *Graph Master* allows students to collect data and create their own graph.
- *Math Arena* is a collection of math activities that reinforces many math concepts.
- *Math Munchers Deluxe* provides practice in basic facts and finding equivalent fractions, decimals, percents, ratios, angles and identifying geometric shapes, factors, and multiples in an arcade-like game.
- *Mighty Math Calculating Crew* poses short answer questions about number operations, 3-dimensional shapes, and money skills.
- *Mighty Math Number Heroes* poses short answer questions about fractions, number operations, polygons, and probability.

BACKGROUND

Applications: An Assessment Unit

> "To ensure deep, high quality learning for all students, assessment and instruction must be integrated so that assessment becomes a routine part of the ongoing classroom activity rather than an interruption."
>
> From the National Council of Teachers of Mathematics *Principles and Standards for School Mathematics,* 2000.

The most powerful indicator of whether a student has acquired new knowledge is if he or she can apply that knowledge to new situations. This assessment unit provides many such opportunities. Students will demonstrate their understanding of concepts studied in the first half of the year by solving problems that arise from several contexts that have strong connections to science and social studies.

Each lesson in this unit reviews, extends, or assesses concepts studied in the first seven units. Lessons 1, 2, 7, and 9 provide opportunities for reflection and review. In Lesson 1 *Experiment Review* students compare and contrast the labs they completed in the first semester. They consolidate their understanding of concepts and strengthen skills such as identifying variables in an experiment and making predictions from graphs. The second lesson *Three in a Row* is a game in which students practice and improve their skills estimating products of decimals. Lesson 7 is a diverse collection of word problems which review skills and concepts that appear on the midyear test. At the end of the unit in Lesson 9, students review and add to their portfolios. They compare work from the beginning of the year to more recent work in this unit.

The remaining lessons give a balanced picture of students' learning by including an open-ended task

in which students must communicate mathematically, a long task that takes several days to complete, and traditional tests that cover a wide range of content. These lessons parallel the assessment activities in Units 1 and 2 so that you can evaluate students' progress since the beginning of the year. For example, in order to document improvement in students' communication skills, compare their write-ups of the problem-solving task *Stack Up* in Unit 2 to the reports they write analyzing data in Lesson 4 *Florence Kelley's Report.* The lab *Searching the Forest* in Unit 1 and other labs can be compared to the lab *Comparing Lives of Animals and Soap Bubbles* in Lesson 6. The midyear test is made up of short items covering content from each of the units, and the Daily Practice and Problems includes a test of the multiplication and division facts.

The diverse nature of the assessment activities in this unit reflects the balance of skills and concepts studied so far this year. The varied sources of information gathered in this unit will make your assessment of student progress more reliable and, significantly, the activities allow students to continue their learning while providing multiple opportunities for students to demonstrate their mathematical knowledge.

Resources

- *Assessment Standards for School Mathematics.* National Council of Teachers of Mathematics, Inc., Reston, VA, 1995.
- Behr, Merlyn J., and Thomas R. Post. "Teaching Rational Number and Decimal Concepts." In Thomas R. Post (ed.), *Teaching Mathematics in Grades K–8: Research Based Methods.* Allyn and Bacon, Boston, 1992.
- *Principles and Standards for School Mathematics.* National Council of Teachers of Mathematics, Reston, VA, 2000.
- Stenmark, J. K., V. Thompson, and R. Cossey. *Family Math.* Lawrence Hall of Science, University of California, Berkeley, CA, 1996.

Assessment Indicators

- Can students collect, organize, graph, and analyze data?
- Can students make and interpret bar graphs and point graphs?
- Can students translate between graphs and real-world events?
- Can students use numerical variables?
- Can students choose appropriate methods and tools to calculate (calculators, pencil and paper, or mental math)?
- Can students solve open-ended problems and communicate solution strategies?
- Can students use fractions, decimals, and percents to represent the same quantity?
- Do students choose appropriately whether to find an estimate or an exact answer?
- Do students demonstrate fluency with the multiplication and division facts?

OBSERVATIONAL ASSESSMENT RECORD

(A1) Can students collect, organize, graph, and analyze data?

(A2) Can students make and interpret bar graphs and point graphs?

(A3) Can students translate between graphs and real-world events?

(A4) Can students use numerical variables?

(A5) Can students choose appropriate methods and tools to calculate (calculators, pencil and paper, or mental math)?

(A6) Can students solve open-ended problems and communicate solution strategies?

(A7) Can students use fractions, decimals, and percents to represent the same quantity?

(A8) Do students choose appropriately whether to find an estimate or an exact answer?

(A9) Do students demonstrate fluency with the multiplication and division facts?

(A10) _____

Name	A1	A2	A3	A4	A5	A6	A7	A8	A9	A10	Comments
1.											
2.											
3.											
4.											
5.											
6.											
7.											
8.											
9.											
10.											
11.											
12.											
13.											

Name	A1	A2	A3	A4	A5	A6	A7	A8	A9	A10	Comments
14.											
15.											
16.											
17.											
18.											
19.											
20.											
21.											
22.											
23.											
24.											
25.											
26.											
27.											
28.											
29.											
30.											
31.											
32.											

Daily Practice and Problems

Applications: An Assessment Unit

A DPP Menu for Unit 8

Eight icons are used to designate the subject matter of the DPP items. Each DPP item may fall into one or more of the categories listed below. The icons appear in the Teacher Notes column in each of the DPP items. Below is a brief menu of the DPP items included in Unit 8.

N Number Sense	**✖** Computation	**🕐** Time	**◈** Geometry
D–G, J, K, N–P, R	D, F, K, L, P	N	A, H
⁵ₓ⁷ Math Facts	**$** Money	**⚖** Measurement	**▨** Data
B, C, I, K, M, Q	O, R	A, H	J, R

Two DPP items are included for each class session listed in the Unit Outline. The first item is always a Bit and the second is either a Task or a Challenge. The *Daily Practice and Problems and Home Practice Guide* in the *Teacher Implementation Guide* includes information on how and when to use the DPP. A *Scope and Sequence Chart* for the Daily Practice and Problems for the year can also be found in the *Teacher Implementation Guide*.

Review and Assessment of Math Facts

By the end of fourth grade, students in *Math Trailblazers™* are expected to demonstrate fluency with all the multiplication and division facts. The DPP for this unit continues the systematic approach to reviewing these facts. This unit reviews all five groups of facts—the 5s and 10s, the 2s and 3s, the squares, the 9s, and the last six facts (4×6, 4×7, 4×8, 6×7, 6×8, and 7×8).

DPP item B instructs students to quiz each other on all of the multiplication facts using the *Triangle Flash Cards*. (One group of facts flash cards was distributed in the *Discovery Assignment Book* following the Home Practice in Units 2–6.) After students sort the multiplication facts, they should record their progress with these facts on clean copies of the *Multiplication Facts I Know* chart. Then, they should quiz each other on all of the division facts and begin new *Division Facts I Know* charts. Ask students to compare their new charts with those they updated in Units 2–7. Since these charts serve as a record of students' progress with

the facts, have students place these new charts in their portfolios.

Encourage students to practice only the facts they did not circle on their new charts. They can take home their *Triangle Flash Cards* for these facts, or they can make a new set of cards for these facts using the *Triangle Flash Card Master,* which follows the Home Practice in the *Discovery Assignment Book.*

At the end of the unit, a test is administered on a mixture of multiplication and division facts (see DPP Item Q). The test immediately follows the DPP. Using the results of the test, students should update their new *Multiplication Facts I Know* and *Division Facts I Know* charts. *Note:* If a particular fact is not on the test (e.g., 4×3) but students correctly answered a related fact ($12 \div 4$), students may circle both of the facts on their charts. Throughout second semester, students can continue to practice those facts they have not yet circled on their charts by using the *Triangle Flash Cards*. Blackline masters of the *Multiplication Facts I Know* and *Division Facts I Know* charts can be found in Lesson Guide 2 of Unit 2.

For more information about the distribution and assessment of the math facts, see the TIMS Tutor: *Math Facts* in the *Teacher Implementation Guide.* Also refer to Unit 2 Lesson Guide 2 and the DPP guide in the *Unit Resource Guide* for Unit 2. All the *Triangle Flash Cards, Triangle Flash Card Master,* and *Facts I Know* charts are available in the *Grade 5 Facts Resource Guide.*

Students may solve the items individually, in groups, or as a class. The items may also be assigned for homework.

Student Questions	Teacher Notes

A Measuring Area

1. Rectangle ABCD has a length of 6 cm and a width of 8 cm. What is its area?

2. Rectangle JKLM is 20 cm by 4.8 cm. How many times greater is its area than rectangle ABCD?

TIMS Bit

1. 48 sq cm

2. two times greater; 96 sq cm

Multiplication and Division Facts

TIMS Task

With a partner, use the *Triangle Flash Cards* to quiz each other on the multiplication facts. Have your partner cover the shaded number (the product). Use the two uncovered numbers to solve a multiplication fact. As you are quizzed, sort the cards into three piles: those facts you know well and can answer quickly, those you know using a strategy, and those you need to learn. Then, circle the facts you know well and can answer quickly on a clean copy of the *Multiplication Facts I Know* chart.

Next, quiz each other on the division facts. To quiz you on the division facts, have your partner cover the numbers in the circles first and then the numbers in the squares. Solve a division fact with the two uncovered numbers. Sort the cards and record your progress on a clean copy of the *Division Facts I Know* chart.

Make a list of the facts you have not yet circled on both your charts. Take the flash cards for these facts home so you can practice them. Your teacher will tell you when the test on these facts will be given.

Students can take home the flash cards for the facts they need to practice, or they can make cards for those facts on copies of the *Triangle Flash Card Master,* which follows the Home Practice in the *Discovery Assignment Book.* Part 1 of the Home Practice reminds students to take home these newly prepared flash cards to study for the test.

The *Multiplication Facts I Know* and *Division Facts I Know* charts were distributed in the *Unit Resource Guide* for Unit 2 Lesson 2. See this Lesson Guide for more information.

Inform students when the test on these facts will be given. This test, which assesses students on multiplication and division facts, is administered as DPP Item Q. A blackline master of the test immediately follows the DPP.

All the *Triangle Flash Cards, Triangle Flash Card Master, Facts I Know* charts, and *Multiplication and Division Fact Inventory Test* are available in the *Grade 5 Facts Resource Guide.*

Student Questions	Teacher Notes

 Fact Practice I

Find *n* to make each number sentence true.

A. $5 \times 8 = n$ B. $3 \times n = 21$

C. $36 \div 6 = n$ D. $n \times 5 = 10$

E. $10 \times 4 = n$ F. $20 \div n = 4$

G. $12 \div 3 = n$ H. $9 \times 6 = n$

I. $n \times 8 = 64$

TIMS Bit

A. 40   B. 7

C. 6   D. 2

E. 40   F. 5

G. 4   H. 54

I. 8

Practicing the Operations

Solve the following using paper and pencil. Estimate to make sure your answers are reasonable.

A. $62 \times 48 =$ B. $871 \div 6 =$

C. $36.3 \times 0.5 =$ D. $8243 - 738 =$

E. $21.8 \times 5 =$ F. $8.2 \times .47 =$

G. $76 \times 200 =$ H. $34 \times 800 =$

I. $8294 + 5088 =$

TIMS Task

A. 2976   B. 145 R 1

C. 18.15   D. 7505

E. 109   F. 3.854

G. 15,200   H. 27,200

I. 13,382

Equivalent Fractions

Find the equivalent fractions.

A. $\frac{3}{5} = \frac{?}{10}$ B. $\frac{3}{4} = \frac{?}{12}$

C. $\frac{2}{5} = \frac{8}{?}$ D. $\frac{5}{10} = \frac{?}{2}$

E. $\frac{10}{12} = \frac{5}{?}$ F. $\frac{1}{3} = \frac{?}{12}$

G. $\frac{5}{9} = \frac{?}{36}$ H. $\frac{7}{10} = \frac{?}{100}$

TIMS Bit

A. $\frac{3}{5} = \frac{6}{10}$ B. $\frac{3}{4} = \frac{9}{12}$

C. $\frac{2}{5} = \frac{8}{20}$ D. $\frac{5}{10} = \frac{1}{2}$

E. $\frac{10}{12} = \frac{5}{6}$ F. $\frac{1}{3} = \frac{4}{12}$

G. $\frac{5}{9} = \frac{20}{36}$ H. $\frac{7}{10} = \frac{70}{100}$

Student Questions	Teacher Notes

 Wall Painting

Michael's family painted the living room and dining room walls. Michael painted $\frac{1}{8}$ of the walls. His sister painted $\frac{1}{4}$ of the walls. Dad painted $\frac{3}{8}$ of the walls. Mom finished the project.

Write three math questions you can ask about Michael's family project. Exchange your problems with a partner or present them to the class to solve.

TIMS Challenge

Answers will vary.
Sample questions:

What fraction of the work did Mom complete? ($\frac{1}{4}$)

Who did the most work? (Dad)

Who did the second most? (sister and Mom)

How much more did Dad do than Michael? ($\frac{2}{8}$ or $\frac{1}{4}$)

What fraction of the project was completed by the children? ($\frac{3}{8}$)

 Quick Change

Change the following fractions to decimals and then to percents.

A. $\frac{23}{100}$ B. $\frac{3}{4}$

C. $\frac{30}{50}$ D. $\frac{68}{100}$

E. $\frac{5}{10}$ F. $\frac{2}{8}$

G. $\frac{9}{100}$ H. $\frac{2}{40}$

TIMS Bit N

Calculators should be available. Discuss students' strategies. For example, to change $\frac{2}{8}$ to a decimal, students can divide $2 \div 8 = 0.25$. Or, they can reduce $\frac{2}{8}$ to $\frac{1}{4}$, then write $\frac{1}{4} = \frac{25}{100} = 0.25$.

A. 0.23; 23%

B. 0.75; 75%

C. 0.6; 60%

D. 0.68; 68%

E. 0.5; 50%

F. 0.25; 25%

G. 0.09; 9%

H. 0.05; 5%

Student Questions	Teacher Notes

 Slab-Maker Problem

You need a protractor and centimeter ruler to complete this task. Follow the instructions below to create quadrilateral CDEF.

Make side DE 5 cm long.

Make ∠ D be 95°.

Make side CD 7 cm long.

Make side EF 3 centimeters shorter than side CD.

TIMS Task

Answers will vary. One possible solution:

 Fact Practice II

Find *n* to make each number sentence true.

A. $10 \times n = 90$

B. $16 \div 2 = n$

C. $3 \times 5 = n$

D. $28 \div 4 = n$

E. $4 \times n = 36$

F. $50 \div n = 10$

G. $6 \times 2 = n$

H. $24 \div 3 = n$

I. $7 \times n = 63$

TIMS Bit

A. 9   B. 8

C. 15   D. 7

E. 9   F. 5

G. 12   H. 8

I. 9

Student Questions	Teacher Notes

 Letter Chances

TIMS Challenge

1. Write down your full name (first, last, and, if you like, middle name). If you cut out all the letters of your names and put them in a bowl, list the probability of choosing each letter that appears in your name. For example, if your name is Roberto Ruiz, the chance of choosing an R is $\frac{3}{11}$. The chance of choosing an O is $\frac{2}{11}$. The chance of choosing a B is $\frac{1}{11}$.

2. What is the probability that you will choose a vowel from the letters in your name?

3. What is the probability that you will choose a letter in the first half of the alphabet (A–M)?

4. What is the probability that you will choose one of the last five letters in the alphabet?

Answers will vary.

Sample answers based on the name Roberto Ruiz.

1. Probability of choosing:
   R $\frac{3}{11}$, O $\frac{2}{11}$, B $\frac{1}{11}$, E $\frac{1}{11}$,
   T $\frac{1}{11}$, U $\frac{1}{11}$, I $\frac{1}{11}$, Z $\frac{1}{11}$

2. $\frac{5}{11}$

3. $\frac{3}{11}$

4. $\frac{1}{11}$

 Fact Practice III

TIMS Bit

Find n to make each number sentence true.

A. $70 \times 6 = n$ B. $90 \times 90 = n$

C. $3000 \div 6 = n$ D. $14,000 \div 200 = n$

E. $40 \times 400 = n$ F. $56,000 \div 80 = n$

G. $30 \times n = 180$ H. $5000 \times 9 = n$

I. $800 \div 10 = n$

A. 420   B. 8100

C. 500   D. 70

E. 16,000   F. 700

G. 6   H. 45,000

I. 80

Adding and Subtracting Fractions

A. $\frac{3}{6} + \frac{2}{6} =$

B. $\frac{2}{3} + \frac{1}{5} =$

C. $\frac{1}{4} - \frac{1}{6} =$

D. $\frac{5}{8} - \frac{1}{4} =$

E. $\frac{3}{8} - \frac{1}{8} =$

F. $\frac{1}{2} - \frac{2}{5} =$

TIMS Task

A. $\frac{5}{6}$ B. $\frac{13}{15}$

C. $\frac{1}{12}$ D. $\frac{3}{8}$

E. $\frac{2}{8}$ or $\frac{1}{4}$ F. $\frac{1}{10}$

M **Fact Practice IV**

Find n to make each number sentence true. Then, name one other fact in the same fact family.

A. $9 \times 2 = n$

B. $30 \div 5 = n$

C. $7 \times 7 = n$

D. $32 \div 8 = n$

E. $10 \times 7 = n$

F. $6 \times 8 = n$

G. $27 \div 3 = n$

H. $8 \times 9 = n$

I. $24 \div 4 = n$

TIMS Bit

A. 18; $2 \times 9 = 18$;
$18 \div 2 = 9$;
$18 \div 9 = 2$

B. 6; $30 \div 6 = 5$;
$6 \times 5 = 30$;
$5 \times 6 = 30$

C. 49; $49 \div 7 = 7$

D. 4; $32 \div 4 = 8$;
$4 \times 8 = 32$;
$8 \times 4 = 32$

E. 70; $7 \times 10 = 70$;
$70 \div 10 = 7$;
$70 \div 7 = 10$

F. 48; $8 \times 6 = 48$;
$48 \div 8 = 6$;
$48 \div 6 = 8$

G. 9; $27 \div 9 = 3$;
$9 \times 3 = 27$;
$3 \times 9 = 27$

H. 72; $9 \times 8 = 72$;
$72 \div 8 = 9$;
$72 \div 9 = 8$

I. 6; $24 \div 6 = 4$;
$6 \times 4 = 24$;
$4 \times 6 = 24$

Student Questions	Teacher Notes

 A Busy School Day!

1. On an average school day, Jackie spends six hours in school. What percent of her day is spent in school?

2. Jackie practices piano one hour on a school day. What fraction of the day does she spend practicing piano?

3. Jackie spends $\frac{1}{3}$ of a day sleeping. How many hours does she sleep?

4. What fraction of Jackie's day is left after school, piano, and sleep? More or less than $\frac{1}{2}$ of a day?

5. Write a similar story using your own daily activities.

TIMS Challenge

1. 25%
2. $\frac{1}{24}$
3. 8 hours
4. $\frac{9}{24}$; less than half
5. Answers will vary.

 Estimating with Money

Estimate the answers to the following problems.

A. $34.56 + $72.35

B. $0.39 + $1.76

C. $0.58 × 8

D. $275.34 − $56.23

Explain your strategy for B.

TIMS Bit

Estimates will vary.

A. over $100

B. $2.15

C. $4.80

D. $225

Possible response: 39¢ is close to 40¢ and $1.76 is close to $1.75. $1.75 plus 25¢ is $2.00. 40¢ − 25¢ is 15¢. Add 15¢ to $2.00 for $2.15.

Student Questions	Teacher Notes

 Number Puzzles

A. I am 3 tenths less than 5 times 7. Who am I?

B. I am twice the sum of 3.4 and 2.1. Who am I?

C. I am less than 10 but more than 5. If you skip count by two-tenths (.2) starting at 0 you get me. The digit in the ones' place is the same as the digit in the tenths' place. My ones' digit is a multiple of 4.

TIMS Challenge

A. 34.7

B. 11

C. 8.8

 Multiplication and Division Fact Inventory Test

Students take a test that contains the facts from all five groups of facts studied in Units 2–8—the 5s and 10s, 2s and 3s, square numbers, 9s, and the last six facts.

Students should have two pens or pencils of different colors ready. During the first four minutes of the test, students write their answers using one color pen or pencil. Encourage students first to answer all the facts they know well and can answer quickly. Then, they should go back and use strategies to solve the rest. After four minutes have passed, give students more time to complete the remaining items with the other color pen or pencil.

Using the results of the test, students should update their new *Multiplication* and *Division Facts I Know* charts.

TIMS Bit

The test follows DPP Item R. It lets you and your students see which multiplication and division facts they still need to study. We recommend 4 minutes for this test.

Students can continue to use the *Triangle Flash Cards* to practice the facts they have not yet circled. Students will continue to practice math facts in the DPP.

Students may include their tests in their portfolios.

Currency

The currency in the European Union is called a Euro. In 2002, 1 Euro was worth 90 cents in the United States. Make a graph to show the number of Euros and their value in the U.S. Graph Number of Euros on the horizontal axis and Value in U.S. Dollars and Cents on the vertical axis.

1. How much were 30 Euros worth in U.S. money?

2. If you trade $30.00 of U.S. money for Euros, about how many Euros will you receive?

1. $27.00

2. Almost 35 Euros

Name _____ Date _____

Multiplication and Division Fact Inventory Test

You will need two pens or pencils of different colors. Use the first color when you begin the test. When your teacher tells you to switch pens, finish the test using the second color.

$5 \times 5 =$	$24 \div 6 =$	$10 \times 7 =$	$15 \div 3 =$
$8 \times 7 =$	$20 \div 10 =$	$7 \times 7 =$	$10 \times 3 =$
$28 \div 4 =$	$54 \div 9 =$	$36 \div 6 =$	$9 \times 5 =$
$5 \times 2 =$	$20 \div 5 =$	$8 \times 8 =$	$60 \div 6 =$
$4 \times 2 =$	$24 \div 8 =$	$2 \times 7 =$	$10 \times 10 =$
$10 \times 9 =$	$16 \div 4 =$	$9 \times 9 =$	$16 \div 2 =$
$8 \times 4 =$	$42 \div 7 =$	$9 \times 4 =$	$10 \times 5 =$
$3 \times 3 =$	$35 \div 7 =$	$7 \times 9 =$	$48 \div 6 =$
$6 \div 3 =$	$3 \times 6 =$	$27 \div 3 =$	$10 \times 4 =$
$72 \div 8 =$	$6 \times 5 =$	$12 \div 4 =$	$7 \times 3 =$
$18 \div 2 =$	$40 \div 8 =$	$2 \times 2 =$	$80 \div 8 =$
$12 \div 6 =$			

LESSON GUIDE 1

Experiment Review

Estimated Class Sessions: 1

Students review the labs they completed during the first seven units by recounting various elements of each lab: variables, number of trials, type of graph, problems solved, etc. To help them recall each lab, they use their *Student Guides* and work collected in their portfolios. The class discusses the differences and similarities of the experiments.

Key Content

- Comparing and contrasting the following elements of different laboratory investigations:

    measurement procedures

    number of trials

    problems solved

    types of graphs

    variables

Key Vocabulary

bar graph
point graph
trial
variable

Daily Practice and Problems: Bit for Lesson 1

A. Measuring Area (URG p. 10)

1. Rectangle ABCD has a length of 6 cm and a width of 8 cm. What is its area?

2. Rectangle JKLM is 20 cm by 4.8 cm. How many times greater is its area than rectangle ABCD?

DPP Task is on page 26. Suggestions for using the DPPs are on page 26.

Materials List

Print Materials for Students

	Math Facts and Daily Practice and Problems	Activity	Homework
Student Books			
Student Guide		*Experiment Review* Page 270	
Discovery Assignment Book	*Triangle Flash Card Master* Pages 131–134	*Experiment Review Chart* Pages 135–136	Home Practice Part 1 Page 127 and *Triangle Flash Card Master* Pages 131–134
Teacher Resources			
Facts Resource Guide	Use the *Triangle Flash Card Master* to create and review facts as needed DPP Item 8B		
Unit Resource Guide	DPP Items A–B Pages 10–11		

available on Teacher Resource CD

All Transparency Masters, Blackline Masters, and Assessment Blackline Masters in the Unit Resource Guide are on the Teacher Resource CD.

Supplies for Each Student

student portfolio

Materials for the Teacher

Distance vs. Time Graph Transparency Master (Unit Resource Guide) Page 28
large sheet of paper for class chart or transparencies of *Experiment Review Chart* Activity Pages (Discovery Assignment Book) Pages 135–136

Developing the Activity

The *Experiment Review* Activity Page in the *Student Guide* provides a context for a class discussion reviewing the labs completed during the year. Professor Peabody is reminded of the lab *Distance vs. Time* from Unit 3 as he times students running the 50-yard dash at a school field day.

During this activity, the class makes a list of the labs they have completed so far this year. Then, each of the labs can be assigned to a group of students for review. Begin the review with a whole-class discussion of the lab *Distance vs. Time* using **Question 2** as a guide. A transparency master of a sample graph for *Distance vs. Time* has been provided to help you review the lab.

> **TIMS Tip**
>
> If your class did not complete the lab *Distance vs. Time*, begin the discussion using a different lab.

Question 3 asks students to use their *Student Guide* and their portfolios to make a list of all the labs they remember working on during the year. After completing this list, assign each group of students one or two labs to review using **Question 2** as their guide. The *Experiment Review Chart* Activity Pages in the *Discovery Assignment Book* will help organize students' review information. This chart can then be used to compare and contrast the experiments.

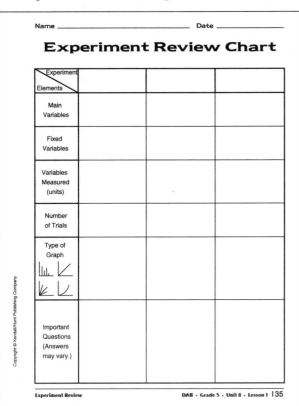

Discovery Assignment Book - Page 135

 Experiment Review

Professor Peabody volunteered to be a timer at the Bessie Coleman Elementary School field day. He timed students as they ran the 50-yard dash. For each student, he recorded the time it took them to run the distance. As he timed each student, he remembered a lab he had worked on some months ago.

 Discuss

1. Which lab does Professor Peabody remember?

2. Answer the following questions about the lab. You may use your *Student Guide* or your portfolio to help you.
   A. What variables did you study in the lab?
   B. Did you have to keep any variables the same so that the experiment would be fair? If so, which ones?
   C. Did you measure anything? If so, what did you measure? What units did you use?
   D. How many trials did you do? If you did more than one trial, tell why.
   E. Describe your graph.
   F. What were the most important problems you solved using your data and your graph?

3. Use your *Student Guide* and your portfolio to make a list of the labs you completed. One or more labs will be assigned to your group. Answer each part of Question 2 for these labs. Use the *Experiment Review Chart* Activity Pages in the *Discovery Assignment Book* to organize your work.

270 SG · Grade 5 · Unit 8 · Lesson 1   Experiment Review

***Student Guide* - Page 270**

Name		Date	
Experiment Elements			
Main Variables			
Fixed Variables			
Variables Measured (units)			
Number of Trials			
Type of Graph			
Important Questions (Answers may vary.)			

136 DAB · Grade 5 · Unit 8 · Lesson 1   Experiment Review

***Discovery Assignment Book* - Page 136**

When all the groups have completed their reviews, each group should make a report to the class. The information from all the groups can be organized on a class chart using large chart paper or transparencies of the *Experiment Review Chart* Activity Pages, as shown in Figure 1. Note that the sample responses to **Question 2** for *Distance vs. Time* are shown in the third lab column of the chart. Your class answers may vary from the responses shown here.

Experiment / Elements	Eyelets	Searching the Forest	Distance vs. Time	Spreading Out	A Day at the Races	Flipping Two Coins
Main Variables	number of eyelets/ number of pairs of shoes	color/number of tiles pulled	distance and time	number of drops/area of spot	time/ distance/ speed	number of heads/ percent of sample
Fixed Variables	definition of eyelets	sample size, rules for setting up bags	pace, timing procedure	size of drop, type of towel, type of liquid, procedure for dropping liquid	timing procedure, distance in 6-yard race, time in 3-second race	procedure for flipping coins, same coins
Variables Measured (units)	none	none	time in seconds, distance in yards	area in sq cm	time in seconds, distance in feet	none
Number of Trials	1	3	3	3	3	10, 100, 1000
Type of Graph						
Important Questions (Answers may vary.)	How many eyelets on all the shoes in the class?	Predict the number of tiles of each color in the bag.	Find the speed that a person walks.	Predict the area of a spot made with a different number of drops.	Compare speeds of students walking, running, etc.	Predict the percent of times heads will come up when flipping two coins many times.

Figure 1: *A sample experiment review class chart*

After all of the groups have reported and the information is displayed, continue discussion using the following questions:

- *When doing an experiment, why do you need to keep some variables fixed?* (To be able to look for patterns and make predictions using the main variables in an experiment, other variables must be held fixed. Otherwise, we won't know which variable caused the change in the experimental data. Students often think of holding variables in an experiment fixed as "keeping the experiment fair." For example, to be able to make predictions about the distance a person can walk in a certain time, the person's pace must remain the same as he or she travels. In *Spreading Out,* students looked for the relationship between the number of drops of water and the area of the spot made on a paper towel. To keep the experiment fair, it is necessary to use the same brand of paper towels. Otherwise, the size of the drops may vary due to the change in paper towel brand as well as the number of drops.)

- *Why do we often have to do more than one trial when doing an experiment?* (One reason scientists use multiple trials is to check on large errors in measurement and to control fixed variables. Since error is often inevitable, scientists use multiple trials so they can average out the error. However, if large errors in measurement are not likely, one trial may suffice.)

- *How are point graphs used to make predictions?* (If the data points lie close to a straight line, a line can be drawn which fits the points. This line is called the best-fit line. You can use this line to make predictions using interpolation or extrapolation. You may wish to show an example of interpolation or extrapolation using the transparency of the *Distance vs. Time Graph.*)

- *Name two experiments which are alike. How are they alike? How are they different?* (While answers may vary for this question, possible student responses follow. *Eyelets* and *Searching the Forest* are alike because they both use bar graphs. In *Eyelets,* you can use the graph to find out which number of eyelets is most common or least common. In *Searching the Forest,* you can use the graph to predict which color of tile is most common or least common in the bag. *Distance vs. Time* and *A Day at the Races* are similar because they use a line on a graph to find the speed that a person travels. In *Distance vs. Time,* each person walks the same distance as they are timed. In *A Day at the Races,* each person moves in a different way as he or she is timed. Each person travels for either a specific period of time or a specific distance.)

Daily Practice and Problems: Task for Lesson 1

B. Task: Multiplication and Division Facts (URG p. 11)

With a partner, use the *Triangle Flash Cards* to quiz each other on the multiplication facts. Have your partner cover the shaded number (the product). Use the two uncovered numbers to solve a multiplication fact. As you are quizzed, sort the cards into three piles: those facts you know well and can answer quickly, those you know using a strategy, and those you need to learn. Then, circle the facts you know well and can answer quickly on a clean copy of the *Multiplication Facts I Know* chart.

Next, quiz each other on the division facts. To quiz you on the division facts, have your partner cover the numbers in the circles first and then the numbers in the squares. Solve a division fact with the two uncovered numbers. Sort the cards and record your progress on a clean copy of the *Division Facts I Know* chart.

Make a list of the facts you have not yet circled on both your charts. Take the flash cards for these facts home so you can practice them. Your teacher will tell you when the test on these facts will be given.

Journal Prompt

Which two experiments did you like the best? What did you like about each one? How are they alike? How are they different?

Suggestions for Teaching the Lesson

Math Facts

DPP item B reviews all of the multiplication and division facts.

Homework and Practice

- DPP Bit A reviews area.
- Assign Part 1 of the Home Practice which asks students to use *Triangle Flash Cards* with a family member to review the multiplication and division facts they need to study.

Answers for Part 1 of the Home Practice can be found in the Answer Key at the end of this lesson and at the end of this unit.

Name _____ Date _____

Unit 8: Home Practice

Part 1 *Triangle Flash Cards:* **All the Facts**

Study for the test on the multiplication and division facts. Take home the flash cards for the facts you need to study.

Ask a family member to choose one flash card at a time. To quiz you on a multiplication fact, he or she should cover the corner containing the highest number. Multiply the two uncovered numbers.

To quiz you on a division fact, your family member can cover one of the smaller numbers. One of the smaller numbers is circled. The other has a square around it. Use the two uncovered numbers to solve a division fact.

Ask your family member to mix up the multiplication and division facts. He or she should sometimes cover the highest number, sometimes cover the circled number, and sometimes cover the number in the square.

Your teacher will tell you when the test on the facts will be.

Part 2 **Practicing the Operations**

1. Use paper and pencil to solve the following problems. Estimate each answer to make sure it is reasonable. Show your work on a separate sheet of paper.
   A. $72 \times 61 =$ B. $0.43 + 7.6 =$ C. $3804 \div 7 =$ D. $61 \times 0.29 =$

2. Estimate the following answers. Describe your strategy for each.
   A. $78,000 \div 40$

   B. $104,000 \div 27$

   C. 9821×14

   D. $178 \times 324,000$

Discovery Assignment Book - Page 127

AT A GLANCE

Math Facts and Daily Practice and Problems

Complete items A–B of the DPP. Item A reviews area. Item B reviews multiplication and division facts.

Developing the Activity

1. Read the opening paragraph on the *Experiment Review* Activity Page in the *Student Guide*.
2. Review the lab *Distance vs. Time* using **Question 2** on the *Experiment Review* Activity Page.
3. Students work in groups to review other labs completed throughout the year using their *Student Guides,* portfolios, **Question 2** on the *Experiment Review* Activity Page, and the *Experiment Review Chart* in the *Discovery Assignment Book.*
4. Each group reports its review information to the class, and the class creates a table showing the components of each lab.
5. Using the prompts in the Lesson Guide, lead a class discussion. Students compare and contrast labs to find similarities and differences.

Homework

Assign Part 1 of the Home Practice.

Notes:

Distance vs. Time Graph

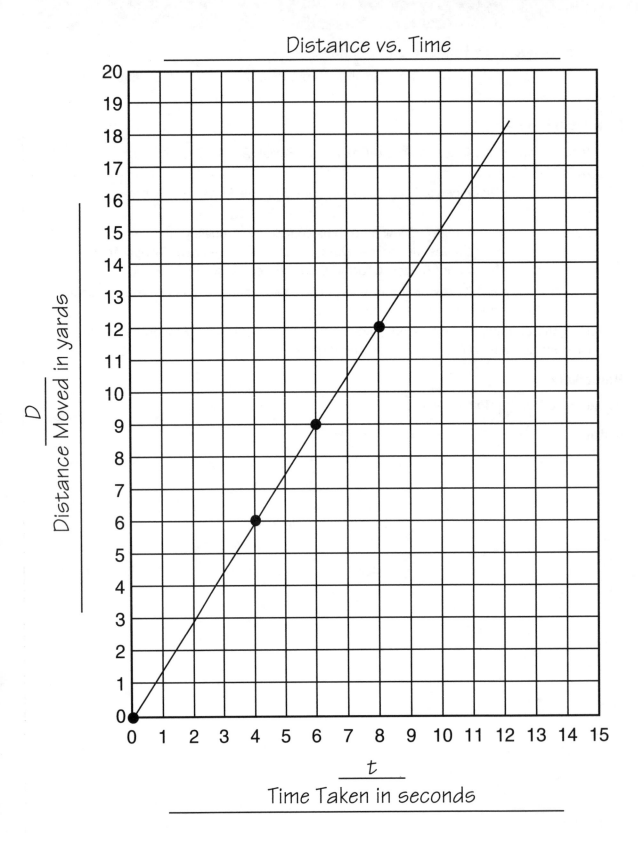

Distance vs. Time

Student Guide

Questions 1–3 (SG p. 270)

I. *Distance vs. Time*

2. **A.** distance, time, and speed

   B. pacing, timing procedure, etc.

   C. Yes, we measured time in seconds and distance in yards.

   D. We did 3 trials to make sure that our data was accurate.

   E. The graph is a point graph with a line that starts at (0 seconds, 0 yards) and goes uphill.

   F. We found the speed at which a student walks.

3. *See the Experiment Review Chart in Figure 1 in Lesson Guide 1.

Discovery Assignment Book

Experiment Review Chart (DAB pp. 135–136)

*See Figure 1 in Lesson Guide 1 for a sample table.

*Answers and/or discussion are included in the Lesson Guide.
**Answers for all the Home Practice in the *Discovery Assignment Book* are at the end of the unit.

OPTIONAL LESSON

There are no Daily Practice and Problems items for this lesson.

LESSON GUIDE
Three in a Row

Estimated Class Sessions: 1

Students play a game that involves estimating the product of decimals.

Key Content

*   Estimating products of decimals.
*   Using fractions and decimals to represent the same quantity.

Materials List

Print Materials for Students

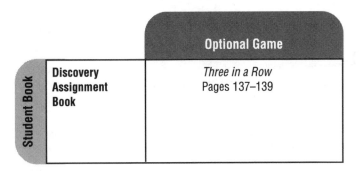

		Optional Game
Student Book	**Discovery Assignment Book**	*Three in a Row* Pages 137–139

Supplies for Each Student

8–10 game markers or tokens of one color
calculator

Materials for the Teacher

Transparency of the game board on the *Three in a Row* Game Pages (Discovery Assignment Book) Page 139

Developing the Activity

Introduce the game by reading the *Three in a Row* Game Pages in the *Discovery Assignment Book*. Demonstrate the game by playing with a student on the overhead using a transparency of the game board. To play this game, each pair of students needs only one game board from the *Discovery Assignment Book*. A player chooses two factors from the factor frame and finds their product using a calculator. (If they want, players may choose one factor and multiply it by itself: i.e., $4.93 \times 4.93 \approx 25$.) The player then covers the square with the number closest to the product on his or her calculator display. The first student to cover three squares in a row, horizontally, vertically, or diagonally, is the winner.

This is a game of estimation and strategy—students should look for patterns as they multiply the factors they choose. After students have had an opportunity to play, discuss the strategies they used to choose their factors. This game can be sent home or used in an activity center.

 TIMS Tip

For game tokens, students can use two colors of centimeter cubes, two kinds of beans, or small scraps of paper with their initials.

Suggestions for Teaching the Lesson

Math Facts

Remind students to practice the multiplication and division facts using their *Triangle Flash Cards*.

Homework and Practice

Students can play the game at home with a family member or friend.

Extension

Students can create their own game boards.

Resource

This game is based on a game entitled *Calculator Game Board: Multiplication* from *Family Math*, written by Jean Kerr Stenmark, Virginia Thompson, and Ruth Cossey. *Family Math* is published by the Lawrence Hall of Science, University of California, Berkeley, California.

Name _____ Date _____

Three in a Row

This is a game for two players.

Materials
- one calculator per player
- 8–10 game markers or tokens of one color or shape for each player
- one factor frame and product board per student pair

Directions
1. Player One selects two factors from the factor frame and finds their product with a calculator. He or she may select two different factors or use the same factor twice.
2. One of the player's markers is placed on the product board on the square with the number that is closest to the product of the two factors.
3. Player Two chooses two factors and follows the same steps described above.
4. Two markers may not occupy the same space.
5. The game continues until one player has three markers in a row, horizontally, vertically, or diagonally.

Discovery Assignment Book - Page 137

Name _____ Date _____

Game Board

Factor Frame						
0.493	0.109	4.93	109	49.3	0.01	493

Product Board

10	500	2500	5
250	0.05	1	25,000
5000	50,000	25	50
2	0.005		

Discovery Assignment Book - Page 139

AT A GLANCE

Math Facts

Remind students to practice their facts at home using their *Triangle Flash Cards.*

Developing the Activity

1. Read and review the directions for the game on the *Three in a Row* Game Pages in the *Discovery Assignment Book.*
2. Use a transparency of the game board in the *Discovery Assignment Book* to demonstrate the game.
3. Student pairs play the game.
4. After students play the game, discuss strategies students used to choose factors.

Homework

Have students play the game at home.

Notes:

Discovery Assignment Book

Three in a Row (DAB pp. 137–139)

*See Lesson Guide 2 for a discussion of the game.

*Answers and/or discussion are included in the Lesson Guide.

**Answers for all the Home Practice in the *Discovery Assignment Book* are at the end of the unit.

URG • Grade 5 • Unit 8 • Lesson 2 • Answer Key 33

LESSON GUIDE 3

Florence Kelley

Estimated Class Sessions: 1

Part 1 of the lesson is an *Adventure Book* story about Florence Kelley, a prominent social reformer who worked at Hull House in Chicago around 1900. She documented social problems through survey data.

Part 2 of the lesson is a discussion of Florence Kelley's data in the *Student Guide*. The story and discussion provide the context for the open-ended assessment problem in Lesson 4 *Florence Kelley's Report*.

One of the problems Kelley documented in the late 1800s was the employment of young children. The *Adventure Book* begins with a fact-based account of Francesca, a young immigrant girl who is mentioned in Kelley's survey notes. Francesca takes classes in English at Jane Addams's Hull House where Florence Kelley is the English teacher.

The story shifts to Kelley's work. Horrified by the ill treatment of children in factories and sweatshops, Kelley is determined to prove the extent of the problem by collecting data and writing fact-filled reports for the government. Implicit in the story are the ideas that math and science are powerful tools for measuring social phenomena and that gathering data is the first step in identifying areas that need improvement. Kelley's survey method is described and one of her original data tables is presented as an illustration. The story ends optimistically with Kelley's prediction—based on her data—that the number of children employed in Illinois will decrease.

Key Content

- Connecting math and science to real-world events.
- Organizing and analyzing data.

Key Vocabulary

immigrant
settlement house
sweatshops

Materials List

Print Materials for Students

	Math Facts and Daily Practice and Problems	Activity	Homework
Student Guide (Student Books)		*Florence Kelley* Pages 271–272	
Discovery Assignment Book (Student Books)			Home Practice Part 5 Page 129
Adventure Book (Student Books)		*Florence Kelley* Pages 47–60	
Facts Resource Guide ⊙ (Teacher Resources)	DPP Item 8C		
Unit Resource Guide ⊙ (Teacher Resources)	DPP Items C–D Page 12		

⊙ available on Teacher Resource CD

All Transparency Masters, Blackline Masters, and Assessment Blackline Masters in the Unit Resource Guide are on the Teacher Resource CD.

Supplies for Each Student

calculator

Materials for the Teacher

Increase in Work Done: Third Annual Report Transparency Master (Unit Resource Guide) Page 42

Developing the Activity

Students should read the *Adventure Book* through first to enjoy the story. Then, use the discussion prompts to discuss the details of the story.

Historical Note

Supreme Court Justice Felix Frankfurter once described Florence Kelley as *"the woman who probably had the largest single share in shaping the social history of the United States during the first thirty years of this century."* While many female reformers of her day organized protests against the government, Kelley chose instead to work with the government in order to effect the passing of legislation in favor of her causes.

Kelley was among the first social scientists to use rigorous survey methods to collect demographic data and among the first to analyze such data and use it in meaningful ways. Her reports to the government were therefore highly effective and influential. Her Illinois factory reports resulted in the passage of laws that prohibited the employment of children under 14 and established the limit of an 8-hour workday for women and children. After seven years at Hull House in Chicago, Florence Kelley moved to New York to help lead the National Consumers League, where she continued to fight poor conditions in factories and sweatshops by organizing consumer boycotts. Kelley was also prominent in women's suffrage and civil rights movements.

Discussion Prompts

Page 54

- *Why did the government want a survey of the neighborhood?*

The government wanted to gather precise data on the living and working conditions of the poor. It wanted to know what problems most needed attention. It wanted data that could later be used to see whether conditions had improved or worsened.

- *Why was the survey important to Florence Kelley?*

She wanted to convince the public and lawmakers that child employment was a real problem. She understood the power that facts and numbers would give to her arguments for reforms.

Page 55

- *How young were some of the children that Florence Kelley found working?*

She found children as young as three years old working. She saw toddlers pulling basting threads out of clothing. (You may need to define the term basting threads for students.)

 Florence Kelley

Jane Addams smiled calmly at her spirited friend. "Ah, then you will be very interested in this letter from the Illinois Bureau of Labor Statistics. They would like you to write a report on the sweatshops of Chicago."

Kelley was immediately interested. "What exactly do they want?" she asked, as she skimmed through the letter.

"It is a huge task," admitted Addams. "They want you to make at least 1000 visits in the neighborhood—go to shops, factories, businesses, and homes and ask the people a long list of questions. That way, the government will be able to gather precise data on what living and working conditions are like for the poor."

Kelley jumped up and began to pace the room. "Yes! This is the kind of research I've been saying should be done! By collecting actual numbers, and by doing it again in future years, we will be able to show whether things are getting better or worse. This is exactly the kind of data that agencies need if they are to plan effective programs to help the poor! Investigating the sweatshops will provide real data to convince the public and the lawmakers that child labor is a real problem."

Addams was not surprised at Kelley's enthusiasm. "I knew you would see the importance of this survey. That was why I recommended you for the job."

"Oh, thank you, Miss Addams!" Kelley exclaimed. "I can't wait to get started!"

In the years that followed, Florence Kelley continued to gather data. Her surveys included factories and households as well as the sweatshops. She and her

54   **AB · Grade 5 · Unit 8 · Lesson 3**

Adventure Book - Page 54

Florence Kelley

assistants spent many long days trudging the streets of Chicago. They knocked on doors, wrote down what they saw, and asked people questions.

They saw homes that were neat and clean and homes that were bare and dirty. Some apartments had no windows. The air inside smelled of coal stoves and cooking grease. Many had no running water or toilets. Some of the factories were even worse, with their loud and dangerous machines. Some people even lived in the same rooms in which they operated small businesses or factories. Here children as young as three years old could be found hard at work beside their parents. Even toddlers could pull the basting threads out of clothing that had been stitched by their mothers.

AB · Grade 5 · Unit 8 · Lesson 3   55

Adventure Book - Page 55

Kelley and her workers talked to hundreds of people and asked many questions. They asked how many children were in each family and where the people worked. They found out how much money each family earned and what languages they spoke. They learned where people had been born and whether they could read and write. They took careful notes and kept a record of every answer.

In the course of her investigations, Florence Kelley was able to prove that great numbers of children were working instead of going to school. These children were poor and uneducated and often worked long hours in terrible conditions. By using her survey data to support her arguments, she convinced many more people that there was a serious problem and that something should be done about it.

However, Kelley did not believe that the United States government in Washington, D.C., would be able to change this anytime soon. She decided to ask the Illinois state legislators to investigate for themselves, in the hope that they would pass state laws against child labor. She wrote reports and made speeches. She even took the lawmakers on tours of the worst factories to show them firsthand what children were being exposed to.

Adventure Book - Page 56

In the summer of 1893, Illinois passed its first factory law. The law made it illegal for children to work more than eight hours a day and illegal for children under the age of fourteen to work at all. There was also a requirement that factories be inspected to make sure they were obeying the new law. Florence Kelley was appointed the first Chief Inspector of Factories in Illinois, a job she energetically carried out for four years.

Adventure Book - Page 57

Discussion Prompts

Page 56

- *What variables did Florence Kelley study in her survey? Label each variable as numerical or categorical.*

Number of children in a family. (Numerical)

Where people worked. (Categorical)

How much money families earned. (Numerical)

Languages spoken. (Categorical)

Where people were born. (Categorical)

Number of children who worked. (Numerical)

- *How did Florence Kelley use the information she collected?*

She used the data to convince people that there was a serious problem. She wrote reports and made speeches to convince lawmakers to make laws addressing the problem of child labor.

Page 57

- *What law did Illinois pass in 1893? What did the law say?*

In 1893, Illinois passed its first factory law. The law made it illegal for children to work more than 8 hours a day and illegal for children under the age of fourteen to work at all. The factories had to be inspected to make sure they were obeying the law. Florence Kelley was the first Chief Factory Inspector of Illinois.

Discussion Prompts

Page 58

- *What did Florence Kelley do as Chief Factory Inspector?*

She wrote a report every year that included all the facts she collected.

Page 60

- *How did the report affect the lawmakers and the factory owners?*

It was important for the lawmakers and for the public to know about problems in the factories. Florence Kelley believed that if people knew about a problem, they would want to solve it. Writing the reports also showed the government that the inspectors were doing the job they were hired to do. Factory owners who were breaking the law were named in the reports and this bad publicity caused them to lose some customers. In order to keep their customers happy, owners began to comply with the law.

 Florence Kelley

Four years later:

Each year that she worked as Chief Factory Inspector, Florence Kelley wrote a long report to the governor. It included all the facts she had collected in that year. One day soon after the publication of her Third Annual Report, she strode into Jane Addams's office without even knocking.

"Dearest Miss Addams,—I've been looking over some of the survey data for the last few years—just take a look at the numbers in the 'Increase in Work Done' data table! Look at the numbers of children who are employed."

Addams had long become used to Kelley's ways and did not seem to mind the interruption. She cast her eye down the page of tables that Kelley was holding out to her. "Hmmm," she said, not quite understanding. "But it looks to me as though there are more children employed now than there were last year."

Adventure Book - Page 58

 Florence Kelley

Jane Addams was happy to agree. "I am sure you are right," she said. "By exposing what the factories and sweatshops are doing, you have gotten the public on our side. Businessmen respect the power of public opinion. To keep their customers, they have to listen and make changes."

Florence Kelley fairly twinkled with glee. She banged her fist happily on Jane Addams's desk, making her jump. "I can't wait to see next year's figures! If this trend continues, it will prove that new laws and careful research can bring about changes in society."

Adventure Book - Page 60

Florence Kelley

As part of her job as Chief Inspector of Factories in Illinois, Florence Kelley wrote a report with all the facts she collected during the year. Here is the data table for her third report.

Third Annual Report
of the
Factory Inspectors of Illinois

Increase in Work Done

Year	Places inspected	Men employed	Women employed	Children employed	Total employed
1895...........................	4,540	151,075	30,670	8,624	190,369
1894...........................	3,440	97,600	24,335	8,130	130,065
Increase................	1,100	53,475	6,335	494	60,304
1895...........................	4,540	151,075	30,670	8,624	190,369
1893...........................	2,362	52,480	17,288	6,456	76,224
Increase................	2,178	98,595	13,382	2,168	114,145

1. Study the data table.
   A. How many children were employed in 1895?
   B. Where did you find this information?
   C. How many children were employed in 1894? 1893?
   D. Was there an increase or decrease in the number of children employed from 1894 to 1895?
   E. Was the number of children employed in 1894 more or less than the number employed in 1893? How many more or less?

2. What do the other columns in the data table tell you?

Student Guide - Page 271

---

3. A. How many places were inspected in 1895? 1894? 1893?
   B. Was there an increase or decrease in the number of places inspected from 1894 to 1895?
   C. Was the number of places inspected in 1894 more or less than the number inspected in 1893? How many more or less?

4. In the story Florence Kelley studies the Third Annual Report and says,

   " . . . I think these numbers show a trend, . . . a trend toward a reduction in the number of children employed. And I predict that because of the new law that this trend will continue."

   A. Do the numbers in the table show a trend toward fewer numbers of children employed? Why or why not?
   B. Was her prediction a good one? Use the data in the table to support your thinking.

Student Guide - Page 272

Discussing the Data

Use the questions on the *Florence Kelley* Activity Pages in the *Student Guide* to lead a discussion on the data table in Florence Kelley's third report to the government. (A transparency master of the data is located at the end of the Lesson Guide.) The table is a copy of the actual table Florence Kelley put in her published report in 1895. *Questions 1–3* familiarize students with the table. Note that the number of children employed in 1895 is listed twice in the table *(Questions 3A–3B).* Be sure students can locate the number of places inspected and the number of children employed for each year on the table.

Question 4 asks students to interpret the data. In the story Florence Kelley predicts that the number of children employed will decrease. Students must decide, based on the data in the table, if this prediction is a good one. If students look carefully at the data, they will see that the number of children employed actually increased each year. However, during the same three years, the number of places inspected also increased each year. Using the data in the table and subtraction, we see that 1674 more children were employed in 1894 (8130 children) than in 1893 (6456 children). However, during the same years 1078 more places were inspected. The table shows that even though 1100 more places were inspected in 1895 than 1894, only 494 more children were employed. Since the increases in the number of children employed are smaller each year even as the number of inspections grows, students can reason that Florence Kelley's prediction is a good one. The trend toward the reduction in the number of children employed will continue.

These questions set the stage for the assessment problem in the next lesson. To complete the assessment, students will be given a data table from Kelley's fourth report in 1896. They will interpret the data and write a report as if they were Kelley.

> ### Journal Prompt
> If you had to write a report showing Florence Kelley's data, how would you arrange the data table? Make your own data table with Florence Kelley's data.

Suggestions for Teaching the Lesson

Math Facts

DPP item C practices multiplication and division facts using variables in number sentences.

Homework and Practice

- Assign DPP item D which practices estimation and operations.
- Assign Part 5 of the Home Practice which reviews reading and interpreting data in a bar graph.

Answers for Part 5 of the Home Practice can be found in the Answer Key at the end of this lesson and at the end of this unit.

Assessment

Use Lesson 4 *Florence Kelley's Report* to assess students' abilities to analyze and display data as well as communicate mathematically.

Resources

- Addams, Jane. *Twenty Years at Hull-House.* Signet, New York, NY, 1999.
- Goldmark, Josephine. *Impatient Crusader: Florence Kelley's Life Story.* Greenwood Publishing Group, Westport, CT, 1981.
- *Hull-House Maps and Papers.* Ayer Co., New Haven, CT, 1970.
- Sklar, Kathryn Kish. *Florence Kelley and the Nation's Work: The Rise of Women's Political Culture, 1830–1900.* Yale University Press, New Haven, CT, 1995.
- *First Annual Report of the Factory Inspectors of Illinois, for the Year Ending December 15, 1893.* H. W. Rokker, Springfield, IL, 1894.
- *Second Annual Report of the Factory Inspectors of Illinois, for the Year Ending December 15, 1894.* Ed. F. Hartman, Springfield, IL, 1895.
- *Third Annual Report of the Factory Inspectors of Illinois, for the Year Ending December 15, 1895.* Ed. F. Hartman, Springfield, IL, 1896.
- *Fourth Annual Report of the Factory Inspectors of Illinois, for the Year Ending December 15, 1896.* Phillips Bros., Springfield, IL, 1897.

Daily Practice and Problems: Task for Lesson 3

D. Task: Practicing the Operations
(URG p. 12)

Solve the following using paper and pencil. Estimate to make sure your answers are reasonable.

A. $62 \times 48 =$

B. $871 \div 6 =$

C. $36.3 \times 0.5 =$

D. $8243 - 738 =$

E. $21.8 \times 5 =$

F. $8.2 \times .47 =$

G. $76 \times 200 =$

H. $34 \times 800 =$

I. $8294 + 5088 =$

Name _____ Date _____

Part 5 How Long Are Names?
Mr. Moreno's class conducted two surveys in the fifth-grade class next door. The students collected two sets of data:

- The number of letters in their first names.
- The total number of letters in their first and last names.

As the class was just about finished graphing the data, the school bell rang. The next day they found that their data tables were mistakenly erased from the chalkboard. The graphs were still there. However, the students realized that they forgot to give each graph a title.

1. Write a title for each graph. Choose titles that will match each graph with the correct survey.

2. Describe each graph in words. Where are the bars? How tall are the bars?

3. Write a note to the class explaining how you were able to match the graphs with the two surveys.

4. Mr. Moreno's class collected data on the number of letters in their own first names. They made a graph titled, "Number of Letters in First Names in Two Classes." Describe this graph. Where are the bars? How tall are the bars?

APPLICATIONS: AN ASSESSMENT UNIT   DAB · Grade 5 · Unit 8 129

Discovery Assignment Book - Page 129

Increase in Work Done: Third Annual Report

Third Annual Report
of the
Factory Inspectors of Illinois

Increase in Work Done

Year	Places inspected	Men employed	Women employed	Children employed	Total employed
1895..........................	4,540	151,075	30,670	8,624	190,369
1894..........................	3,440	97,600	24,335	8,130	130,065
Increase.................	1,100	53,475	6,335	494	60,304
1895..........................	4,540	151,075	30,670	8,624	190,369
1893..........................	2,362	52,480	17,288	6,456	76,224
Increase.................	2,178	98,595	13,382	2,168	114,145

Student Guide

Questions 1–4 (SG pp. 271–272)

1. **A.** 8624 children

   B. *In the column labeled children employed and in the rows labeled 1895. (Note: The information is in the table twice.)

   C. 1894: 8130 children; 1893: 6456 children

   D. increase

   E. more; 1674 more children

2. The number of places inspected, the number of men employed, the number of women employed, and the total employed for the years 1893, 1894, and 1895.

3. **A.** 1895: 4540 places, 1894: 3440 places, 1893: 2362 places

   B. increase

   C. more; 1078 places

4. **A.** *Yes, the number of children employed does not increase as fast as the number of places inspected.

   B. *Yes, the number of children employed between 1893–1894 increased by 1674 children while the number of places inspected increased by 1078. From 1894 to 1895, while the number of places inspected increased at about the same rate (1100 more places inspected), the number of children employed only increased by 494 children.

Discovery Assignment Book

**Home Practice (DAB p. 129)

Part 5. How Long Are Names?

Questions 1–4

1. Answers will vary. The graph on the left can be titled "Number of Letters in First Names" and the graph on the right can be titled "Number of Letters in First and Last Names."

2. Answers will vary. Some students may mention that for the data in the graph on the left there is a larger range for the number of letters (10–16 letters) but shorter bars. The graph on the right has a smaller range for the number of letters (4–7) but more data for the numbers within that range (taller bars).

3. Answers will vary. Students will probably mention that the data for the graph on the left show a larger number of letters in names than the graph on the right and is therefore the graph showing the letters for first and last names combined.

4. Answers will vary. Possible response: The bars on the graph will be between 3 and 8 letters. The bars will be about twice as tall as the bars on the graph for one class.

---

*Answers and/or discussion are included in the Lesson Guide.

**Answers for all the Home Practice in the *Discovery Assignment Book* are at the end of the unit.

Florence Kelley's Report

Estimated Class Sessions: 1–2

The Adventure Book *Florence Kelley* from Lesson 3 provides a context for this assessment. In the book, Florence Kelley collects data on child employment during the years 1893–1895 and publishes the data in a report to the governor. This lesson is an assessment in which students graph and analyze similar data for the years 1893–1896.

Key Content

- Graphing and analyzing data.
- Using data to solve problems.
- Using the Student Rubrics: *Knowing* and *Telling* to self-assess problem-solving skills.
- Solving open-response problems and communicating solution strategies.

Curriculum Sequence

Before This Unit

Analyzing Data. Analysis of data is an integral part of *Math Trailblazers*. Beginning in Unit 1 of fifth grade, students analyzed their own data in Lesson 1 in the lab *Eyelets,* and they analyzed bar graphs in Lesson 3 *Analyzing Data.* They used the Student Rubric: *Knowing* for the first time in fifth grade to guide them as they completed the lab *Searching the Forest* in Lesson 5. They continued to analyze data in labs in Units 2, 3, 4, and 7.

Communicating Mathematically. Throughout the curriculum, questions in activities and labs encourage students to communicate their thinking. To help them communicate mathematically, they were introduced to the Student Rubric: *Telling* in Grade 3 and used it extensively in Grade 4. They used the *Telling* rubric for the first time in fifth grade to help them write their problem-solving strategies in the assessment problem *Stack Up* in Unit 2 Lesson 9.

After This Unit

Analyzing Data. Students will continue to collect and analyze data in labs in Units 13, 14, and 16.

Communicating Mathematically. Throughout the remaining units, students will explain their thinking either in class discussion or in writing. In particular, they will write about their problem-solving strategies in assessment lessons in Units 9, 11, and 16.

Materials List

Print Materials for Students

		Math Facts and Daily Practice and Problems	Assessment Activity	Written Assessment
Student Book	**Student Guide**		Student Rubrics: *Knowing* Appendix A and *Telling* Appendix C and Inside Back Cover ⊙	
Teacher Resources	**Unit Resource Guide**	DPP Items E–F Pages 12–13 ⊙		*Florence Kelley's Report* Page 56, 1 per student
	Generic Section ⊙		*Centimeter Graph Paper*, 1–2 per student	

⊙ *available on Teacher Resource CD*

All Transparency Masters, Blackline Masters, and Assessment Blackline Masters in the Unit Resource Guide are on the Teacher Resource CD.

Supplies for Each Student

calculator

Materials for the Teacher

Transparency or poster of *Student Rubric: Knowing* (Teacher Implementation Guide, Assessment section)
Transparency or poster of *Student Rubric: Telling* (Teacher Implementation Guide, Assessment section)
TIMS Multidimensional Rubric (Teacher Implementation Guide, Assessment section)

Before the Activity

To prepare for this assessment, students read the Adventure Book *Florence Kelley* in Lesson 3 and discussed the data she collected using the questions on the *Florence Kelley* Activity Pages in the *Student Guide*.

Developing the Activity

Part 1. Writing the Report

Use the discussion prompts below as a review of the Adventure Book.

*   *How did Florence Kelley convince people that child labor was a serious problem?* (She conducted surveys on the living and working conditions of people in Illinois.)

*   *Illinois passed its first factory law in 1893. What did the law say about children working in factories?* (Children could not work more than eight hours each day. It was illegal for children under fourteen to work at all.)

*   *What was Florence Kelley's job as Chief Factory Inspector?* (She helped inspect the factories and wrote a report to the governor using her data.)

Distribute graph paper and one copy of *Florence Kelley's Report* Assessment Page to each student. Remind students that in the previous lesson they studied the data Florence Kelley included in her Third Annual Report to the governor in 1895. Explain to students that the data table on the assessment page is the data table she included in her fourth report for the years 1893–1896.

Encourage students to use the Student Rubrics: *Knowing* and *Telling* to guide their work. Highlight the sections of the rubrics that particularly apply to the problem. For example, use the *Telling* rubric to remind students to tell what each number refers to (i.e., 2362 factories or 6456 children). Encourage them to explain how the graphs and number sentences help tell the story of the data. Use the *Knowing* rubric to encourage them to show the mathematical ideas in the report in more than one way, including a graph and words. Point out to students that you expect a correct graph with a title, appropriate scales, and carefully labeled axes.

TIMS Tip

Students can work on this assessment in several ways. They can complete the assignment individually or with a partner. Alternatively, partners can discuss the data and decide how to set up their graphs and then each student can write his or her report individually.

As students work, you may need to help some students get started. Make a note of those students who need help and include that information in your evaluation of their work. Use prompts similar to the following:

- *How many children are employed in each year?*
- *What year are the most children employed?*
- *How many places are inspected each year?*
- *Does the data in the table show that the factory law is working?*
- *How can you use a graph to help explain the data in the table?*

Part 2. Scoring Students' Work

When students have drawn their graphs and written their reports, give them an opportunity to revise their work based on your comments. Refer to the student rubrics as needed. For example, you may need to remind students to title their graphs or to tell what each number in the report stands for. Remind students to use their graph as a tool for describing the data and showing the trends in child employment.

You can use the Knowing and Telling dimensions of the *TIMS Multidimensional Rubric* to score students' work. See the Assessment section in the *Teacher Implementation Guide* for more information on using the rubric to evaluate students' writing.

To assist you in scoring students' work, questions specific to the task for these dimensions are listed below.

Knowing

- Does the student understand the task? Does he or she use the data in the table to show how the number of children employed has changed during the years the law has been in effect?
- Can he or she translate between the situation as described in the story, the data table, words, and graphs?
- Did the student draw a graph correctly? Interpret the data correctly?
- Is the student able to track the increases and decreases in the data?
- If applicable, did the student subtract correctly?

Telling

- Is the written response complete and clear?
- Are the arguments logical? Do they follow from the data in the table?
- Does the student refer to the graph in the report, using it to help explain the data?

Content Note

Bar Graph or Point Graph? Either bar graphs or point graphs are appropriate to display this data. Bars are typically used when there are no values in between the data points. A bar graph is appropriate here since there are no years between 1893 and 1894, between 1894 and 1895, etc.

Point graphs are used when there are values between the data points. We can argue that there are values between the years, since there are many days and months between 1894 and 1895. Therefore, plotting points makes sense. If the points form a pattern, we fit a curve or a line to the points to emphasize the patterns in the data.

Three samples of student work follow. Each has been scored using the Knowing and Telling dimensions of the *TIMS Multidimensional Rubric*.

Student A's report.

Florence Kelley

My report is about Florence Kelley and the difference between 1893 and 1896. In 1893 6,456 where wocking (that is not a lot of people wocking) In 1894 more people started wocking, it was up in the 8 thousands. As time went by more people started wocking in 1895, about 8,624 are now wocking in 1895. Now in 1896 it got lower to 7,340 people wocking, that is 1,284 less. (8,624 - 7,340 = 1,284) The places inspected doesn't have alot of jobs for people, but the amount of people is going up witch means there is not alot of places for people wock, so they don't have much money and know place to live. So hopefully people came start building places to wock.

Student A's graph.

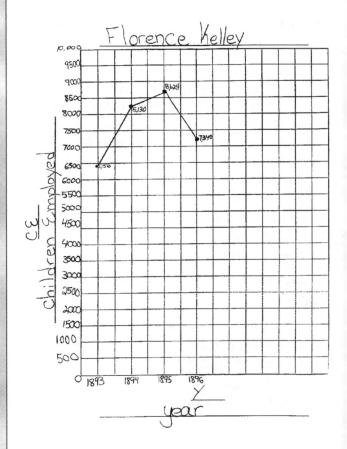

Scoring Student A's work.

Knowing	Level 4	Level 3	Level 2	Level 1
Understands the task's mathematical concepts, their properties and applications…	Completely	Nearly completely	Par̶t̶ially	Not at all
Translates between words, pictures, symbols, tables, graphs, and real situations…	Readily and without errors	With minor errors	With ma̶j̶or errors	Not at all
Uses tools (measuring devices, graphs, tables, calculators, etc.) and procedures…	Correctly and efficiently	Correctly or with minor errors	Incorrectly	Not at all
Uses knowledge of the facts of mathematics (geometry definitions, math facts, etc.)…	Cor̶r̶ectly	With minor errors	With major errors	Not at all

Telling	Level 4	Level 3	Level 2	Level 1
Includes response with an explanation and/or description which is…	Complete and clear	Fairly complete and clear	Perhaps ambiguous or unclear	Totally unclear or irrelevant
Presents supporting arguments which are…	Strong and sound	Logically sound, but may contain minor gaps	Incomplete or logically unsound	Not present
Uses pictures, symbols, tables, and graphs which are…	Correct and clearly relevant	Present with minor errors or somewhat irrelevant	Present with errors and/or irrelevant	Not present or completely inappropriate
Uses terminology…	Clearly and precisely	With minor errors	With major errors	Not at all

Figure 2: *Student A's work and scores on the rubrics*

Knowing—2

Student A had only a partial understanding of the task. She never mentions child employment. However, she knew to compare the numbers in the Children Employed column. She correctly tracked the increases and decreases in these numbers, using subtraction to show the decrease from 1895 to 1896. She translated the data from the table to the graph correctly, but she shows little understanding of what the numbers mean. For example, her interpretation of the data in the Places Inspected column is very confusing.

Telling—2

Student A had a lot of trouble communicating her thinking. When she uses the number of children employed for each year, she refers instead to people working. Her arguments are illogical and, although her graph is correct, it is not relevant to her discussion of the data.

Dear Goverment,
I learned what Florence Kelly wanted to happen to the children employed in math. She wanted for less children employed. Florence Kelly got what she wanted but the numbers I'm about to show might look like from 1893-1896 for children employed it is getter bigger but it's not I'll explain. From 1893 there were 6456 and from 1894 there was 8130 also for 1895 and 1896 there were more children employed. But good because there more places inspected each year. I'm glad because there is a deacrease in children employed. Through 1895 and 1896 there was a decrease of 1284 children employed.

Student B's graph.

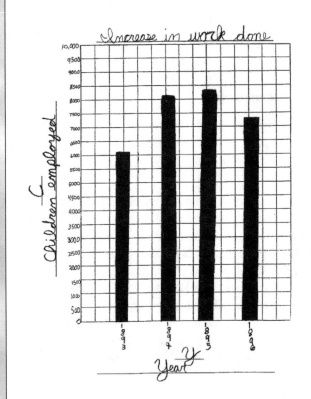

Scoring Student B's work.

Knowing	Level 4	Level 3	Level 2	Level 1
Understands the task's mathematical concepts, their properties and applications…	Com~~pletely~~	Nearly completely	Partially	Not at all
Translates between words, pictures, symbols, tables, graphs, and real situations…	Readily and without errors	With mi~~nor~~ errors	With major errors	Not at all
Uses tools (measuring devices, graphs, tables, calculators, etc.) and procedures…	Correctly and efficiently	Correc~~tly~~ or with minor ~~errors~~	Incorrectly	Not at all
Uses knowledge of the facts of mathematics (geometry definitions, math facts, etc.)…	Correctly	With mi~~nor~~ errors	With major errors	Not at all

Telling	Level 4	Level 3	Level 2	Level 1
Includes response with an explanation and/or description which is…	Complete and clear	Fair~~ly~~ complete and ~~clear~~	Perhaps ambiguous or unclear	Totally unclear or irrelevant
Presents supporting arguments which are…	Strong and sound	Logically sound, but ma~~y~~ contain minor gaps	Incomplete or logically unsound	Not present
Uses pictures, symbols, tables, and graphs which are…	Correct and clearly relevant	Present with minor errors or some-what irrelevant	Present with errors and/or ~~irrelevant~~	Not present or completely inappropriate
Uses terminology…	Clearly and precisely	With mi~~nor~~ errors	With major errors	Not at all

Figure 3: *Student B's work and scores on the rubrics*

Knowing—3

Student B clearly understood the task. He analyzed the child employment data in relation to the number of factories inspected to determine if the numbers of children employed decreased as Florence Kelley predicted in the story. He made connections between the data table, the real situation, and words with few errors. (At one point he says, "for 1895 and 1896 there were more children employed" which is not true. However, he corrects himself in the last line.) He was also able to translate the data into a graph with minor errors.

Telling—3

Student B's response is fairly complete and clear. We can follow his logic, although there are minor gaps, including two statements which are inconsistent. The sentences with child employment data are unclear because he does not label the numbers with "children employed." However, he is able to support his argument, that it "... might look like from 1893–1896 for children employment it is getting bigger but its not" with "because there were more places inspected each year." He includes a graph, but it seems to be irrelevant to his conclusions, since he never mentions it in his writing.

Student C's report.

I think the law is working because as I inspected sweat shops, I saw less children working. I saw looking at my graphs that less children were employed and more places were inspected. It looked something like this.

Student C's graphs.

Scoring Student C's work.

Knowing	Level 4	Level 3	Level 2	Level 1
Understands the task's mathematical concepts, their properties and applications…	Com~~pl~~etely	Nearly completely	Partially	Not at all
Translates between words, pictures, symbols, tables, graphs, and real situations…	(Readily) and without errors	(With minor errors)	With major errors	Not at all
Uses tools (measuring devices, graphs, tables, calculators, etc.) and procedures…	Correctly and efficiently	Correctly or with minor errors	Incorrectly	Not at all
Uses knowledge of the facts of mathematics (geometry definitions, math facts, etc.)… **N/A**	Correctly	With minor errors	With major errors	Not at all

Telling	Level 4	Level 3	Level 2	Level 1
Includes response with an explanation and/or description which is…	Complete and clear	Fairly complete and clear	Perhaps ambiguous or unclear	Totally unclear or irrelevant
Presents supporting arguments which are…	Strong and sound	(Logically sound, but may contain minor gaps)	(Incomplete or logically unsound)	Not present
Uses pictures, symbols, tables, and graphs which are…	(Correct and clearly relevant)	(Present with minor errors or somewhat irrelevant)	Present with errors and/or irrelevant	Not present or completely inappropriate
Uses terminology… **N/A**	Clearly and precisely	With minor errors	With major errors	Not at all

Figure 4: *Student C's work and scores on the rubrics*

Knowing—3

Student C understood that she needed to analyze the data in both the Places Inspected column and the Children Employed column to see if the factory law was effective. Although there was a minor error in one graph (one point is plotted incorrectly), she translated the real situation from the table to graphs to words.

Telling—3

Student C's explanation is fairly complete and clear, although she does not refer to any numbers in her analysis. She supports her argument that "less children were employed and more places were inspected" by referring to her graphs.

Suggestions for Teaching the Lesson

Math Facts

Remind students to practice their math facts using their *Triangle Flash Cards*.

Assessment

- If students include this assessment in their portfolios, they can compare their work on this lesson to their writing for earlier assessment lessons such as *Stack Up* in Unit 2 Lesson 9.

- Use this lesson as an assessment of students' abilities to work together as a group. Tell students that they must help Florence Kelley present the data to the state legislature. Groups can plan and present their reports to the whole class.

- Use DPP Challenge F as an assessment of students' abilities to communicate mathematically as they write math problems and present them to their partner or the class. Evaluate students' abilities to express their solution strategies to classmates' math problems.

AT A GLANCE

Math Facts and Daily Practice and Problems

Complete DPP items E–F which include work with fractions.

Before the Activity

Read and discuss the Adventure Book *Florence Kelley* in Lesson 3.

Part 1. Writing the Report

1. Review the Adventure Book using the discussion prompts in Part 1 of this Lesson Guide.
2. Distribute graph paper and the *Florence Kelley's Report* Assessment Page from the *Unit Resource Guide* to students. Calculators should be available.
3. Review the Student Rubrics: *Knowing* and *Telling*. Encourage students to use them as a guide as they work.
4. Students write their reports.

Part 2. Scoring Students' Work

1. Give students a chance to revise their work based on your comments.
2. Score students' reports using the Knowing and Telling dimensions of the *TIMS Multidimensional Rubric*.
3. Students place their completed assessments in their collection folders.

Assessment

1. Compare this lesson to work on *Stack Up* in Unit 2.
2. Assess students' abilities to work cooperatively.
3. Use DPP item F as an assessment of students' abilities to communicate mathematically.

Notes:

Florence Kelley's Report

Imagine that you are Florence Kelley. It has been four years since the factory law was passed in 1893. As part of your job as Chief Factory Inspector, you must write a report to the governor. Here is the data table for your Fourth Annual Report.

Fourth Annual Report
of the
Factory Inspectors of Illinois

Increase in Work Done
1893–1896

Year	Places inspected	Men employed	Women employed	Children employed	Total employed
1896.........................	6,707	162,019	30,781	7,340	200,140
1893.........................	2,362	52,480	17,288	6,456	76,224
Increase................	4,345	109,539	13,493	884	123,916
Decrease................					
1896.........................	6,707	162,019	30,781	7,340	200,140
1894.........................	3,440	97,600	24,335	8,130	130,065
Increase................	3,267	64,419	6,446		70,075
Decrease................				790	
1896.........................	6,707	162,019	30,781	7,340	200,140
1895.........................	4,540	151,075	30,670	8,624	190,369
Increase................	2,167	10,944	111		9,771
Decrease................				1,284	

Use the data in the table to write a report on child employment from 1893 to 1896. Use at least one graph in your report to help you explain the data.

You may use any of the tools you use in your math class to help you prepare your report. Use the *Knowing* and *Telling* rubrics to guide your work. Write your report on a separate sheet of paper.

Unit Resource Guide

Florence Kelley's Report (URG p. 56)

*See Lesson Guide 4 for samples of student work.

*Answers and/or discussion are included in the Lesson Guide.

**Answers for all the Home Practice in the *Discovery Assignment Book* are at the end of the unit.

URG • Grade 5 • Unit 8 • Lesson 4 • Answer Key 57

6. Quick Change (URG p. 13)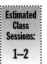

Change the following fractions to decimals and then to percents.

A. $\frac{23}{100}$ B. $\frac{3}{4}$

C. $\frac{30}{50}$ D. $\frac{68}{100}$

E. $\frac{5}{10}$ F. $\frac{2}{8}$

G. $\frac{9}{100}$ H. $\frac{2}{40}$

DPP Task is on page 65. Suggestions for using the DPPs are on page 65.

LESSON GUIDE 5

Life Spans

Estimated Class Sessions: 1–2

Students compare human life span data from 1858 to life span data from 1997. Students are introduced to grouping data into bins or equal intervals. They graph the data and use the graphs to tell the story of the data. This activity prepares students for the assessment lab *Comparing Lives of Animals and Soap Bubbles* in Lesson 6.

Key Content

- Using fractions, decimals, and percents to represent the same quantity.
- Grouping data in bins to see patterns.
- Making and interpreting bar graphs using binned data.
- Translating between graphs and real-world events.
- Connecting mathematics and science to real-world situations.
- Averaging: finding the median.

Key Vocabulary

binning data

Curriculum Sequence

Before This Unit

Binning and Analyzing Data. Students have analyzed data throughout the curriculum. In Grade 4 Unit 13 students collected data on the number of hours students watched TV, binned the data, and graphed the data in a bar graph in order to analyze it. In Unit 1 Lesson 3 of fifth grade, *Analyzing Data,* they compared three sets of data using bar graphs, and they analyzed their own data in the labs *Eyelets* in Lesson 1 and *Searching the Forest* in Lesson 5. In Unit 7 Lesson 9 students used bar graphs to display the data in the probability experiment *Flipping Two Coins.*

Fractions, Decimals, and Percents. Students translated between fractions, decimals, and percents in Unit 7. They used percents to compare sets of data in Lesson 1 *Fractions, Decimals, and Percents* and Lesson 9 *Flipping Two Coins.*

After This Unit

Analyzing Data. Students will continue to analyze data throughout the year using different kinds of graphs. In Unit 14 students will analyze and display data in circle graphs.

Fractions, Decimals, and Percents. Fractions, decimals, and percents are used to build circle graphs in Unit 14.

Materials List

Print Materials for Students

	Math Facts and Daily Practice and Problems	Activity	Homework
Student Books			
Student Guide		*Life Spans* Pages 273–275	
Discovery Assignment Book		*Life Spans Data Tables* Page 141	Home Practice Part 2 Page 127
Teacher Resources			
Unit Resource Guide	DPP Items G–H Pages 13–14 ⊙		
Generic Section ⊙		*Centimeter Graph Paper,* 2 per student	

⊙ *available on Teacher Resource CD*

All Transparency Masters, Blackline Masters, and Assessment Blackline Masters in the Unit Resource Guide are on the Teacher Resource CD.

Supplies for Each Student

calculator

Materials for the Teacher

Graphing Life Spans Transparency Master (Unit Resource Guide) Page 67, optional
Transparency of *Life Spans Data Tables* Activity Page (Discovery Assignment Book) Page 141, optional

Life Spans

The students in Mr. Moreno's classroom are studying the history of the United States. They learned that the United States changed rapidly during the 1900s. During this time many people began working in factories instead of working on farms. Living conditions and sanitation improved for most people. At the same time, the discovery of antibiotics and other improvements in medical care changed the way doctors treat diseases.

The students wondered if these changes had any effect on the length of time people lived. Mr. Moreno suggested that they collect information on the life spans of people before these changes occurred and compare them with life spans of people after these changes occurred. The students decided to compare the life spans of a set of people who lived during the 1800s to the life spans of a set of people who lived during the 1900s.

Brandon and David went to the library to collect data. Brandon looked for obituaries in old newspapers. He looked through many old newspapers from the year 1858 and found 25 death notices which listed the names of the people who died and their age at death. He wrote down the age of each person: 56 yr, 1 yr 3 mo, 54 yr, 9 mo, 27 yr, 42 yr, 2½ mo, 5 yr, 38 yr, 34 yr, 79 yr, 59 yr, 76 yr, infant, 21 yr, 25 yr, 24 yr, 19 yr, 30 yr, 62 yr, 51 yr, 43 yr, 20 yr, 1 yr, and 5 yr.

David looked in more recent newspapers. He found 50 obituaries which gave the age at death. He wrote down these ages which were all given in years: 75, 88, 84, 79, 85, 86, 51, 77, 85, 88, 88, 71, 84, 85, 89, 92, 77, 97, 80, 60, 95, 62, 85, 64, 44, 74, 62, 87, 81, 73, 89, 15, 96, 84, 72, 89, 84, 90, 88, 50, 68, 72, 75, 63, 90, 65, 38, 77, 79, and 73. All the people in David's data set died in February of 1997.

David and Brandon shared their data with the class.

I. Compare the two sets of life spans. What do you notice about the length of the life spans in the 1858 data and the length of the life spans in the 1997 data?

Student Guide - Page 273

Content Note

Binning Data. When there are many values and a wide range of values in a data set, it is often impractical to display the data using a bar graph without grouping the data into intervals or **bins**. For example, suppose a principal of a large school collects data on the number of miles teachers drive to school. He finds that the number of miles teachers drive ranges from 1 to 50 miles and no two teachers drive the same number of miles to school. It is not useful to make a bar graph with a scale of 1 to 50 miles on the horizontal axis and one bar for each different number of miles driven. The horizontal axis would be too long and all the bars would be the same height. It is better to group the data into equal intervals or, as we say, to "bin" the data. In this case, the data can be divided into intervals such as 0–9 miles, 10–19 miles, 20–29 miles, etc. Then a bar can be drawn for each interval. *Note:* The bars are drawn between the lines to show that the data lie within the interval. For example, the first bar tells us that ten teachers drive between 0 and 9 miles to work.

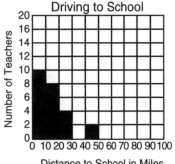

Before the Activity

Students will use fractions, decimals, and percents during this activity. Use DPP item G to review translating fractions to decimals to percents.

Developing the Activity

Part 1. Life Spans

Read the vignette on the *Life Spans* Activity Pages in the *Student Guide.* Discuss the information that David and Brandon gathered at the library, beginning with **Question 1.** Students can see that the ages at death listed in the 1858 data range from infancy to 79 years and the life spans in the 1997 data range from 15 to 97 years.

𝕋IMS Tip

To discourage students from writing in their *Student Guides,* suggest that they write both of the data sets on their own paper. If they work in pairs, one partner can read the numbers while the other writes them down. Then, as you discuss the data, students can check off numbers as needed.

Students may find it difficult to find trends in the data as it is listed in the *Student Guide.* **Question 2** suggests graphing the data as a way to tell the story of the data. It also asks how to set up the graphs. Students may have many suggestions. Help students evaluate the different methods by asking if the graph they propose will help them "tell the story of the data." That is, will the graph help them see the changes in the length of the life spans in the two sets of data?

To make a useful graph, an intermediate step is needed. The data is reorganized in a table so that the number of deaths at each age can be tallied. Also, the data needs to be grouped into intervals that will help illustrate patterns in the data. Use these prompts to guide the discussion:

*   *What do we want to compare?* (Life spans—how long people lived—in the mid-1800s to life spans in the late 1900s. Did people live longer in the twentieth century?)
*   *What data do we need to make this comparison?* (We need to know how many people in each data set lived to each age. For example, how many people lived to be 60? How many lived to be 50?)
*   *How can we find this data?* (Make a new table and tally the number of deaths at each age.)

- *How would you graph this data? What variable would you put on the horizontal axis? What variable would you put on the vertical axis?* (Put the age in years on the horizontal axis and the number of deaths at each age on the vertical axis.)

- *If you made a bar graph of the 1858 data, how would you need to scale the horizontal axis? Is this practical?* (From 0 to 79. No, this scale is not practical since the scale won't fit on the graph paper.)

- *How tall would most of the bars be?* (Most of the bars would be very small. Since they would all be about the same height, they would not give much information. Figure 5 shows what the beginning of a bar graph would look like with the horizontal axis scaled by ones.)

You can suggest to students that they need a new way to organize the data to help them see trends in the data. In the *Student Guide,* Mr. Moreno suggests that students bin the data. Explain that you bin data so it will be easier to graph and so you can see patterns in the data better. Ask students to look at the life span data and suggest possible intervals that can be used *(Question 3).* One suggestion is to use intervals of 10 years. The intervals will then be 0–9 years, 10–19 years, 20–29 years, 30–39 years, and so on until there are bins for all of the data.

2. The students in Mr. Moreno's class found it difficult to compare the two sets of data as David and Brandon reported it. They decided to make two graphs to display the data. How can you set up the graphs to tell the story of the data?

Mr. Moreno suggested that the students **bin** their data. He explained that when you bin data, you look at how data falls within equal intervals. For example, if you measure the height of each person in the class, you can group the data into bins such as 120–129 centimeters tall, 130–139 centimeters tall, 140–149 centimeters tall, 150–159 centimeters tall, and 160–169 centimeters tall. The number of heights in each bin is recorded.

3. A. What intervals can you use to bin the life span data? (*Hint:* Listing the ages on a separate sheet of paper may help you choose your bins.)
   B. What are some reasons to bin data?

4. The students binned the data and recorded the number of life spans in each interval. They knew they had a different number of people in each data set.
   A. How many life spans are in the 1858 data?
   B. How many life spans are in the 1997 data?
   C. What strategies can the students use to compare the data in the two sets?

5. Use the 1858 data to complete a data table like the one shown below. You may use the *Life Spans Data Tables* Activity Page in the *Discovery Assignment Book.* (*Hint:* To tally the data, list the ages on a separate sheet of paper. Then, you can check off each number as you tally.)

A Age (in years)	N Number of Deaths		Fraction of Deaths	Percent of Deaths (to the Nearest Percent)
	Tallies	Number		

Graph

6. For this type of data, mathematicians usually use a bar graph.
   • Make a bar graph of this data.

Student Guide - Page 274

TIMS Tip

The intervals or bins should not overlap and should be the same size. For example, students should not choose intervals from 0–10 years, 10–20 years, or 20–30 years. Using these bins, students will not know where to tally life spans of 10, 20, or 30 years. Choosing the last bin to be "over 60 years" is also problematic, since this bin is larger than the others.

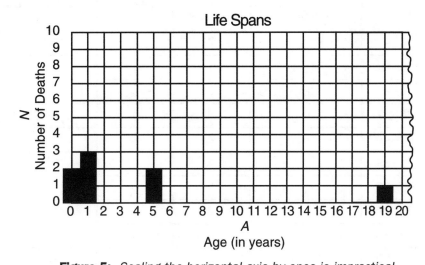

Figure 5: *Scaling the horizontal axis by ones is impractical.*

Life Spans Data Tables

1858 Data Table

A Age (in years)	N Number of Deaths		Fraction of Deaths	Percent of Deaths (to the Nearest Percent)
	Tallies	Number		

1997 Data Table

A Age (in years)	N Number of Deaths		Fraction of Deaths	Percent of Deaths (to the Nearest Percent)
	Tallies	Number		

Life Spans DAB · Grade 5 · Unit 8 · Lesson 5 141

Discovery Assignment Book - Page 141

Question 4 asks students how they can compare data if their samples are different sizes. There are 25 life spans in the 1858 data and 50 life spans in the 1997 data. Students had some experience with this in Unit 7. Remind students that when Lee Yah and her cousin compared data from their class survey on favorite sports (Unit 7 Lesson 1), they found that they could more easily compare the data using decimals and percents. Remind students that when you use percents, one whole equals 100. Therefore, when you convert to percents, you are showing what part, out of 100, of your sample you are considering. This allows you to compare samples of different sizes accurately.

Part 2. Graphing Life Spans Data

Students can use the blank data tables on the *Life Spans Data Tables* Activity Page in the *Discovery Assignment Book* to bin their data ***(Question 5).*** A sample table is shown in Figure 6. Note that the intervals are the same size and that they do not overlap.

> **TIMS Tip**
>
> Remind students that the number of tallies in the 1858 data table should equal 25 and the sum of the percents should equal 100%.

After completing the table, ***Question 6*** asks students to graph the data using a bar graph. However, this graph will be somewhat different from other bar

1858 Data Table

A Age (in years)	N Number of Deaths		Fraction of Deaths	Percent of Deaths (to the Nearest Percent)
	Tallies	Number		
0–9	ЖН II	7	$\frac{7}{25}$	28%
10–19	I	1	$\frac{1}{25}$	4%
20–29	ЖН	5	$\frac{5}{25}$	20%
30–39	III	3	$\frac{3}{25}$	12%
40–49	II	2	$\frac{2}{25}$	8%
50–59	IIII	4	$\frac{4}{25}$	16%
60–69	I	1	$\frac{1}{25}$	4%
70–79	II	2	$\frac{2}{25}$	8%
80–89		0	$\frac{0}{25}$	0%
90–99		0	$\frac{0}{25}$	0%

Figure 6: *1858 data table*

graphs they have made. Students will graph the Percent of Deaths on the vertical axis. Make sure that students scale this axis appropriately. One suggestion is to scale by four percent intervals. The Age in Years will be graphed on the horizontal axis. The lines of the graph will be numbered using the first number of each interval. The spaces between the lines represent the bins or intervals. Students build the bars in these spaces to show that the data falls within the interval (see Figure 7).

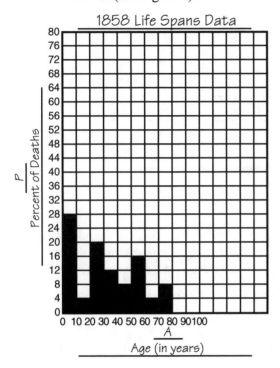

Figure 7: *Graph of life spans from the 1858 data*

The *Graphing Life Spans* Transparency Master shows a sample graph of this data. Before you continue, use students' graphs of the 1858 data to make sure that they understand the procedure for graphing. Students can discuss **Question 7** in small groups and then report their conclusions to the whole class. Encourage students to connect the shape of the graph to the data. For example, they can say that the tallest bar at the beginning of the graph tells us that many people in this set died in early childhood.

Using averages is another way to represent the data. **Question 8** asks students to estimate first the average life span in the 1858 data and then find the median. Since half of the data falls within the first three bars, they can estimate that the average age at death is near 30 years old. To find the median, students will need to order the ages from youngest to oldest and find the middle value (27 years).

Students can work independently or in small groups to complete **Questions 9–12.** Figures 8 and 9 show the data table and graph for the 1997 data. Remind

- Plot the Percent of Deaths on the vertical axis.
- Plot the Age in Years on the horizontal axis.
- Draw the bars between the lines to show that most of the ages fall between the numbers on the horizontal axis.
- When you start graphing the data, your graph might look like the graph to the right.

7. Describe the shape of your graph. The shape of the graph tells the story of the data. Use these questions to help you.
   - Are all the bars about the same height or are some bars much taller than others?
   - Where are the tallest bars, at the beginning, middle, or end of the graph?
   - What do the heights of the bars tell you about life spans in this set of data?

8. A. Use your graph to estimate the average life span for the 1858 data.
   B. Find the median life span for this data.

9. Use the 1997 data to complete a data table like the one in Question 5.

10. Make a bar graph of the 1997 data.
    - Plot the Age in Years on the horizontal axis and the Percent of Deaths on the vertical axis.
    - Use the same scales you used for the graph in Question 6.

11. Describe the shape of this graph. Use the questions in Question 7 to help you tell the story of the data.

12. A. Use your graph to estimate the average life span for the 1997 data.
    B. Find the median life span for this data.

13. Use the graphs to help you compare the two sets of data. What do the graphs tell you about the length of the life spans in the two data sets?

14. What do you think caused the changes in life spans?

Student Guide **- Page 275**

1997 Life Spans Data

A Age (in years)	N Number of Deaths		Fraction of Deaths	Percent of Deaths (to the Nearest Percent)
	Tallies	Number		
0–9		0	$\frac{0}{50}$	0%
10–19	I	1	$\frac{1}{50}$	2%
20–29		0	$\frac{0}{50}$	0%
30–39	I	1	$\frac{1}{50}$	2%
40–49	I	1	$\frac{1}{50}$	2%
50–59	II	2	$\frac{2}{50}$	4%
60–69	卌 II	7	$\frac{7}{50}$	14%
70–79	卌 卌 III	13	$\frac{13}{50}$	26%
80–89	卌 卌 卌 IIII	19	$\frac{19}{50}$	38%
90–99	卌 I	6	$\frac{6}{50}$	12%

Figure 8: *1997 data table*

TIMS Tip

The tallies on the 1997 data table should equal 50 and the sum of the percents should equal 100%.

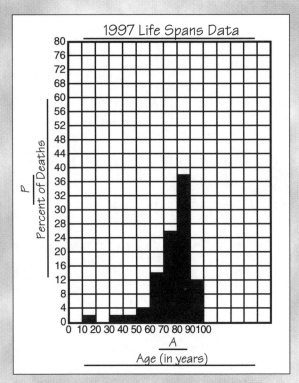

Figure 9: *Graph of life spans from the 1997 data*

students to use the same scales they used for the 1858 graph so they can easily compare the graphs. *Questions 9–12* can also be assigned for homework.

In *Question 11* students are asked to describe the 1997 graph. They should see that the bars are taller as you move to the right on the graph and that there are no bars or very short bars in the first five intervals. This tells us that most people in the 1997 data set lived longer than 50 years and very few people died under the age of 50.

Students are asked to compare the two graphs in *Question 13.* You can use the *Graphing Life Spans* transparency as you discuss this question. Since the shapes of the two graphs are different, the life spans of people in these two samples are also different. On the 1858 graph, there is a tall bar at the very beginning of the graph. The rest of the graph is made up of shorter bars. The tallest bar represents deaths of young children. There are no bars past the age of 80. The 1997 graph shows no deaths for young children. There are short bars in the intervals for the ages 10–60 years. The tallest bars represent deaths between the ages of 70 and 90 years. A small percentage of this data set lived into their 90s. Comparing these two graphs and, therefore, these two data sets, students can say that many more people in the 1858 data set died as children and very few lived long lives. In general, the people in the 1997 data set lived longer lives. This change can also be seen by comparing medians. The median life span of the people in the 1858 data set was 27 years, and the median life span of the people in the 1997 data set was 79.5 years *(Question 12)*.

As students answer *Question 14,* they should think about possible reasons for the change in the shape of the two graphs. Students should understand that in the 1800s, many children died. Of those who survived childhood, many died early in life because of poor living conditions and disease. In the 1900s, living conditions began to improve in the United States. Changes that have had a significant impact on human life spans include the improvement of sanitation conditions which prevented the spread of infectious diseases. These changes include increased use of window screens, accessibility to pure drinking water, and appropriate treatment of raw sewage. There were also improvements in medical care, such as the development of antibiotics which were used to treat infectious diseases. Thus, fewer children died and people now live longer lives.

Suggestions for Teaching the Lesson

Homework and Practice

*   Assign DPP Bit G before the activity for a quick review of converting fractions to decimals to percents.

*   Students can complete the data table and graph for the 1997 data *(Questions 9–12)* as homework.

*   Assign DPP item H as a review of geometry in preparation for the midyear assessment.

*   Assign Part 2 of the Home Practice which provides practice with estimation and computation.

Answers for Part 2 of the Home Practice can be found in the Answer Key at the end of this lesson and at the end of this unit.

Extension

Collect additional life span data. Choose one or more time frames that your class is interested in studying. You may choose to look for data on people who lived during the 1800s and 1900s and compare your data with the data in the lesson. You can gather data from obituaries in newspapers as described in the *Student Guide* or you can gather data from cemeteries. Using information from the headstones, record the birth and death dates for at least 30 to 40 people in each time frame you choose to study. Time frames should not overlap. Graph this data and compare it to the graphs you have already made.

Name _____ Date _____

Unit 8: Home Practice

Part 1 *Triangle Flash Cards:* All the Facts
Study for the test on the multiplication and division facts. Take home the flash cards for the facts you need to study.

Ask a family member to choose one flash card at a time. To quiz you on a multiplication fact, he or she should cover the corner containing the highest number. Multiply the two uncovered numbers.

To quiz you on a division fact, your family member can cover one of the smaller numbers. One of the smaller numbers is circled. The other has a square around it. Use the two uncovered numbers to solve a division fact.

Ask your family member to mix up the multiplication and division facts. He or she should sometimes cover the highest number, sometimes cover the circled number, and sometimes cover the number in the square.

Your teacher will tell you when the test on the facts will be.

Part 2 Practicing the Operations
1. Use paper and pencil to solve the following problems. Estimate each answer to make sure it is reasonable. Show your work on a separate sheet of paper.
   A. $72 \times 61 =$ B. $0.43 + 7.6 =$ C. $3804 \div 7 =$ D. $61 \times 0.29 =$

2. Estimate the following answers. Describe your strategy for each.
   A. $78,000 \div 40$

   B. $104,000 \div 27$

   C. 9821×14

   D. $178 \times 324,000$

APPLICATIONS: AN ASSESSMENT UNIT　　　　　　　**DAB · Grade 5 · Unit 8** 127

Discovery Assignment Book - Page 127

AT A GLANCE

Math Facts and Daily Practice and Problems

Assign DPP items G–H which review fractions, decimals, percents, and geometry.

Part 1. Life Spans

1. Read and discuss the vignette and the data tables on the *Life Spans* Activity Pages in the *Student Guide*. *(Question 1)*
2. Discuss why graphing this data, as presented, would be difficult. Use the prompts in the Lesson Guide to lead a discussion on how to graph the data. *(Question 2)*
3. Introduce binning of data. Explain that this strategy allows work with data that has a broad range. It also makes it easier to see patterns in data. *(Question 3)*
4. Discuss use of percents to compare data when each data set has a different number of data points. *(Question 4)*

Part 2. Graphing Life Spans Data

1. Fill in data tables for the 1858 data using the *Life Spans Data Tables* Activity Page in the *Discovery Assignment Book.* Convert fractions to percents. *(Question 5)*
2. Make a bar graph of this data. Use the transparency to make sure students understand how to scale both axes. Make sure students build the bars between the lines to indicate the bins. *(Question 6)*
3. Discuss the shape of the graph. Use the prompts in the *Student Guide* to connect the shape of the graph to the data. *(Question 7)*
4. Students find the average life span in the 1858 data. *(Question 8)*
5. Students complete *Questions 9–12* that ask them to organize, graph, and analyze the 1997 data.
6. Discuss *Questions 13–14.* Compare the two sets of data using the graphs and medians.

Homework

1. For homework, students can complete the data table and graph for 1997 data. They find the median age at death for this data. *(Questions 9–12)*
2. Assign Part 2 of the Home Practice.

Notes:

Graphing Life Spans

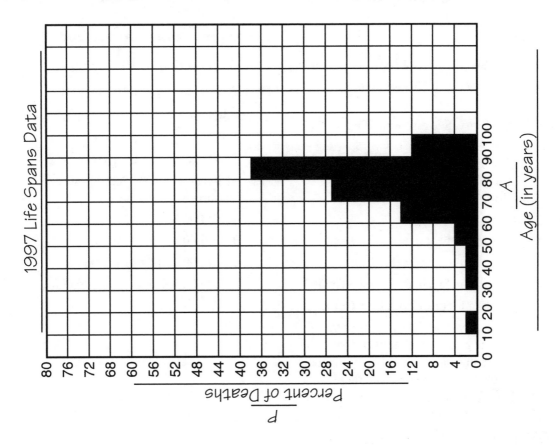

1997 Life Spans Data

Percent of Deaths

Age (in years)

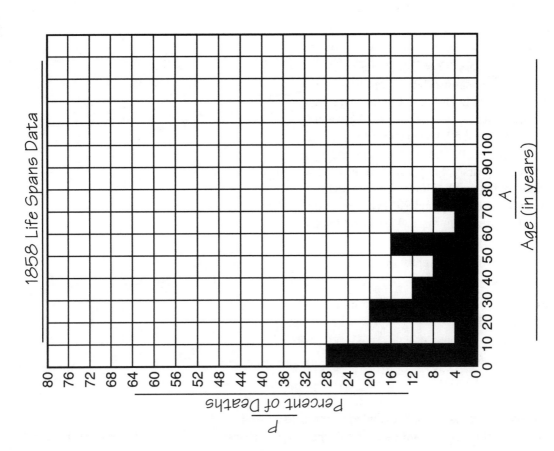

1858 Life Spans Data

Percent of Deaths

Age (in years)

Student Guide

Questions 1–14 (SG pp. 273–275)

1. *Answers will vary. See discussion in Lesson Guide 5.

2. *Answers will vary. See discussion in Lesson Guide 5.

3. *Suggested intervals are 0–9 yr, 10–19 yr, 20–29 yr, 30–39 yr, 40–49 yr, 50–59 yr, 60–69 yr, 70–79 yr.

4. **A.** *25 life spans
    B. *50 life spans
    C. *Use percents to compare the data.

5. *See the data table in Figure 6 in Lesson Guide 5.

6. *See the graph in Figure 7 in Lesson Guide 5.

7. *Answers will vary. The tallest bar is at the beginning of the graph which tells us that many people in this data set died in childhood. All of the other bars are shorter and there are no bars after 80 years of age indicating that few people lived long lives.

8. **A.** *About 30 years old.
    B. *27 years old.

9. *See the data table in Figure 8 in Lesson Guide 5.

10. *See the graph in Figure 9 in Lesson Guide 5.

11. *Answers will vary. There isn't a bar in the first interval indicating there weren't any deaths during early childhood in this data set. There are no bars or very short bars between the ages of 10 and 50, so very few people died under the age of 50. The bars between the ages of 50 and 90 years get larger as you move to the right on the graph. The tallest bars are between the ages of 70 and 90. These bars tell us that most people in the 1997 data set lived long lives.

12. **A.** Answers will vary slightly. About 80 years.
    B. 79.5 years

13. *Answers will vary. See the discussion in Lesson Guide 5.

14. *Answers will vary. See the discussion in Lesson Guide 5.

Discovery Assignment Book

**Home Practice (DAB p. 127)

Part 2. Practicing the Operations

Questions 1–2

1. **A.** 4392   **B.** 8.03
    C. 543 R3   **D.** 17.69

2. Answers will vary. Possible strategies are shown.
    A. $80,000 \div 40 = 2000$
    B. $100,000 \div 25 = 4000$
    C. $10,000 \times 14 = 140,000$
    D. $200 \times 300,000 = 60,000,000$

---

*Answers and/or discussion are included in the Lesson Guide.
**Answers for all the Home Practice in the *Discovery Assignment Book* are at the end of the unit.

LESSON GUIDE

Comparing Lives of Animals and Soap Bubbles

Estimated Class Sessions: 3

This lab extends students' investigations of the life spans of people in Lesson 5. Students collect, graph, and analyze data on the length of time soap bubbles live. They compare the graphs from their classroom experiment showing the "age at death" of bubbles to graphs showing the age at death of animals. They are assessed on their abilities to collect, graph, and analyze data and to use percents in the context of an experiment.

Key Content

- Collecting, organizing, graphing, and analyzing data.
- Using numerical variables.
- Making and interpreting bar graphs using binned data.
- Translating between graphs and real-world events.
- Using fractions, decimals, and percents to represent the same quantity.
- Connecting mathematics and science to real-world situations.
- Using the Student Rubric: *Telling* to self-assess communication skills.

Daily Practice and Problems: Bits for Lesson 6

I. Fact Practice II (URG p. 14)

Find *n* to make each number sentence true.

A. $10 \times n = 90$ B. $16 \div 2 = n$

C. $3 \times 5 = n$ D. $28 \div 4 = n$

E. $4 \times n = 36$ F. $50 \div n = 10$

G. $6 \times 2 = n$ H. $24 \div 3 = n$

I. $7 \times n = 63$

K. Fact Practice III (URG p. 15)

Find *n* to make each number sentence true.

A. $70 \times 6 = n$ B. $90 \times 90 = n$

C. $3000 \div 6 = n$ D. $14,000 \div 200 = n$

E. $40 \times 400 = n$ F. $56,000 \div 80 = n$

G. $30 \times n = 180$ H. $5000 \times 9 = n$

I. $800 \div 10 = n$

M. Fact Practice IV (URG p. 16)

Find *n* to make each number sentence true. Then, name one other fact in the same fact family.

A. $9 \times 2 = n$ B. $30 \div 5 = n$

C. $7 \times 7 = n$ D. $32 \div 8 = n$

E. $10 \times 7 = n$ F. $6 \times 8 = n$

G. $27 \div 3 = n$ H. $8 \times 9 = n$

I. $24 \div 4 = n$

DPP Task and Challenges are on page 75. Suggestions for using the DPPs are on page 75.

Materials List

Print Materials for Students

	Math Facts and Daily Practice and Problems	Assessment Lab	Homework
Student Books — Student Guide		*Comparing Lives of Animals and Soap Bubbles* Pages 276–279 Student Rubric: *Telling* Appendix C and Inside Back Cover ◉	
Student Books — Discovery Assignment Book		*Soap Bubbles Data Table* Page 143 (optional)	Home Practice Parts 3 & 4 Page 128
Teacher Resources — Facts Resource Guide ◉	DPP Items 8I, 8K, and 8M		
Teacher Resources — Unit Resource Guide	DPP Items I–N Pages 14–17 ◉		
Teacher Resources — Generic Section ◉		*Centimeter Graph Paper,* 1 per student	

◉ available on Teacher Resource CD

All Transparency Masters, Blackline Masters, and Assessment Blackline Masters in the Unit Resource Guide are on the Teacher Resource CD.

Supplies for Each Student

calculator

Supplies for Each Student Group

small jar of bubble solution
bubble wand
stopwatch or watch which measures seconds
paper towels

Materials for the Teacher

TIMS Multidimensional Rubric (Teacher Implementation Guide, Assessment section)
Transparency of *Soap Bubbles Data Table* (Discovery Assignment Book) Page 143, optional
Transparency of *Centimeter Graph Paper* (Unit Resource Guide, Generic Section), optional

Developing the Lab

Part 1. Launching the Investigation

Read and discuss the descriptions of the lives of different kinds of animals in the first section of the *Comparing Lives of Animals and Soap Bubbles* Activity Pages in the *Student Guide*. *Question 1* asks students to match three descriptions of the life spans of three kinds of animals with three different graphs showing the percent of animals that die at any given age. Each graph has a characteristic shape. Be sure students can correctly identify each graph. Graph A matches the description of the life spans of American robins, since robins of all ages are equally likely to die. Graph B displays the life spans of humans since tall bars to the right indicate that the majority of humans live a long time. Graph C represents the life spans of oysters, since the bars to the left tell us that most oysters die at a young age. The shape of these graphs will be compared to the shape of a graph showing the percent of bubbles that burst after any given number of seconds.

A.

B.

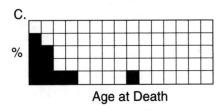

C.

Figure 10: *Graph A is for American robins, Graph B for humans, and Graph C for oysters.*

The second section in the *Student Guide,* Experimenting with Soap Bubbles, discusses the variables and develops the procedure for the experiment. *Question 2* directs students to observe a few bubbles and consider the variables involved in the experiment. The two main variables in the experiment, the time at which a bubble pops and the percent of bubbles that pop after any given number of seconds, are analogous to the age at death of an animal and the percent of

Lives of Animals

The shape of a graph can give important information. In Lesson 5, *Life Spans,* you graphed data on the life spans of people in the United States. You compared the shapes of two graphs. Biologists also gather similar information about animals. They collect data on the age at death of many animals of the same species. Once graphed, these data give important information to the scientist about that species.

Following are brief descriptions of the lives of three different kinds of animals:

Humans. Humans nurture their young until they are old enough to care for themselves. However, babies are at greater risk of illness and disease because their immune systems are still developing. Humans die from disease and accidents as they age, but modern medicine has controlled many diseases, so the majority of people live a long time.

American robins. Robins care for their young until they are old enough to fly and gather food for themselves. From the time they leave the nest, robins of all ages are equally likely to be eaten by predators or to die from accidents. Chance has a much greater effect on how long robins live than it does for other kinds of organisms.

Oysters. Early in life, oysters are very small and have thin shells. Most are eaten by predators when they are very young. As adults with thick shells, surviving oysters live for a very long time.

Student Guide - Page 276

1. Following are three graphs that show the age at which these animals are most likely to die. Find the graph that matches the description for each animal: humans, American robins, and oysters.

Experimenting with Soap Bubbles

Often, scientific experiments are limited by the conditions in a laboratory. As scientists in a classroom, you cannot collect data on the life spans of many kinds of animals. Biologists have found that the shape of a graph showing the "age at death" of soap bubbles resembles the shape of similar graphs for some animals.

In this experiment, you will collect data on the life spans or "age at death" of soap bubbles. Using this data you will make graphs similar to those you made of the life spans of people in Lesson 5. Then, the graphs from your soap bubble data will be compared to the three graphs shown in Question 1.

To collect the data for this experiment, you will measure the time that each bubble lives and then find the percentage of the bubbles that live for a given time.

Discuss

2. Try out your bubble solution. Observe the bubbles. Catch some with your wand and observe them until they pop. What variables are involved in the experiment? What variables do you think affect the life span of a soap bubble?

Student Guide - Page 277

Student Guide - Page 278

deaths at any given age. The following variables are also involved in the experiment since they may affect the life span of a bubble:

• the type of bubble solution,
• whether the bubble is held on a wand or allowed to drop to the ground,
• the ventilation in the room,
• the air temperature,
• the humidity, and
• the size of a bubble.

In **Question 3,** students develop a plan for collecting data.

• To measure accurately the life span of a bubble, they must first decide when a bubble's life begins and ends. To find out how long a bubble will live if it does not hit the ground or another object, they should catch the bubbles on the wand. The moment the bubble lands on the wand and the moment the bubble pops can be defined as the beginning and end of a bubble's life *(Question 3A)*.

• *Question 3B* asks for fixed variables. The type of bubble solution should be the same for all the bubbles and each bubble should be held the same way on the wand (either up or down). Because the temperature, humidity, and movement of the air affect the time bubbles last, it is best to time the bubbles in the classroom away from open windows, air conditioners, or heating vents.

• Since often many bubbles are made with one blow, students will only be able to select one bubble from any group to time with the stopwatch. They should try to select bubbles of the same size and should not choose "double" bubbles *(Question 3C)*.

• *Question 3D* asks students to select a sample size. Twenty or 25 bubbles provide enough data to analyze and both are good numbers to use when finding percents.

• Three students per group work well for this lab. One student can blow the bubbles and catch them on the wand, one can time the bubbles, and one can record the data *(Question 3E)*.

Part 2. Drawing the Picture and Collecting the Data

Question 4 directs students to draw a picture that shows the procedures and identifies the variables. Use the pictures to check that students have a clear idea of the procedures and the variables involved in the experiment. See Figure 11 for an example of a student's labeled drawing. Then, each group should proceed with the investigation as independently as possible so that you can assess their abilities to carry out an experiment.

Figure 11: *Sample of a labeled student picture*

Before students begin collecting data, they should time a few bubbles *(Question 5)*. Since the number of seconds the bubbles live can vary greatly, students will need to bin the data. *Question 6* asks them to use this preliminary data to predict the shape of a graph of the life spans of the bubbles by drawing a sketch or describing the graph in words. The question prompts students to connect the length of time the bubbles last to bars on a graph. They can use the graphs in the *Student Guide* which show the life spans of American robins, oysters, and humans as examples.

The preliminary data from *Question 5* will also give students an idea of the possible values for the length of time the bubbles will last using your brand of bubble solution and given the conditions in your room. Before students begin collecting and recording data, they should fill in the first column of their data tables with intervals *(Question 7)*. Students will need to bin the data so that the scale of the graph is reasonable and so they can look for patterns in the graph. We recommend that students use intervals of five or ten seconds. The sample data in Figure 12 is for 20 bubbles using a commercially available bubble solution. The first column in the data table shows intervals of 10 seconds which are all the same size and do not overlap.

TIMS Tip

Overlapping intervals such as 1–10 seconds and 10–20 seconds should be avoided so that students know where to make a tally mark for 10 seconds. Another common mistake is to make the last interval "greater than 80 seconds," which is not the same size as the other intervals. Note also that the intervals in the sample data table are given to the nearest hundredth of a second to correspond with the readings on a stopwatch. If you only measure the time to the nearest second or tenth of a second, the intervals should be written accordingly.

Name _____ **Date** _____

Soap Bubbles Data Table

Life Spans of Soap Bubbles

t Time in Seconds	Tallies	N Number of Bubbles	P Percent of Bubbles

Comparing Lives of Animals and Soap Bubbles   DAB · Grade 5 · Unit 8 · Lesson 6   143

***Discovery Assignment Book* - Page 143**

Life Spans of Soap Bubbles

t Time in Seconds	Tallies	N Number of Bubbles	P Percent of Bubbles
0.00 – 9.99		0	0%
10.00 –19.99		0	0%
20.00 – 29.99		0	0%
30.00 – 39.99	ΗΗΤ	5	25%
40.00 – 49.99	ΗΗΤ ΙΙ	7	35%
50.00 – 59.99	ΗΗΤ ΙΙ	7	35%
60.00 – 69.99	Ι	1	5%
70.00 – 79.99		0	0%

Figure 12: *Sample data for 20 bubbles*

Part 3. Graphing the Data

Question 9 directs students to make a graph of the data with time (in seconds) on the horizontal axis and the percent of bubbles on the vertical axis. Since this is an assessment lab, students should complete their graphs as independently as possible. Figure 13 is a graph of the sample data. Note the horizontal axis is scaled by 10s since the width of each interval (bin) in the data table is 10 seconds.

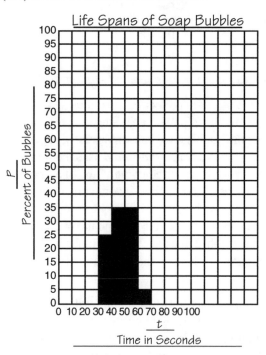

Figure 13: *Graph of the sample data*

Part 4. Analyzing the Data

Questions 10–11 ask students to analyze the shapes of their graphs. To help students plan their responses, review the Student Rubric: *Telling.* Tell them you will use the rubric when you score their work. All the bars on the graph in Figure 13 lie between 30 and 70 seconds and three of the four bars are similar in height. This tells us that the bubbles lived for a long time and all burst after about the same amount of time. Although no bubbles died at a young age, this graph is similar to the graph for humans in the *Student Guide* since, like bubbles, humans are likely to live for a relatively long time and many die at about the same age *(Question 12).* Note that although we have found that the shape of the graphs for the life spans of bubbles usually resembles the graph for humans, different conditions and different bubble solutions may result in graphs with different shapes.

> **Journal Prompt**
> What mathematical skills does a biologist need to know to study the life spans of animals?

Suggestions for Teaching the Lesson

Math Facts

DPP items I, K, and M practice the multiplication and division facts using variables in number sentences.

Homework and Practice

- Assign some or all of the review problems in Lesson 7 for homework.

- DPP items J, L, and N review probability and operations with fractions, decimals, and percents. Assign these items as practice in preparation for the Midyear Test in Lesson 8.

- Assign Parts 3 and 4 of the Home Practice which review the concepts for the midyear test.

Answers for Parts 3 and 4 of the Home Practice can be found in the Answer Key at the end of this lesson and at the end of this unit.

Discovery Assignment Book - Page 128

Daily Practice and Problems: Task & Challenges for Lesson 6

J. Challenge: Letter Chances
(URG p. 15)

1. Write down your full name (first, last, and, if you like, middle name). If you cut out all the letters of your names and put them in a bowl, list the probability of choosing each letter that appears in your name. For example, if your name is Roberto Ruiz, the chance of choosing an R is $\frac{3}{11}$. The chance of choosing an O is $\frac{2}{11}$. The chance of choosing a B is $\frac{1}{11}$.

2. What is the probability that you will choose a vowel from the letters in your name?

3. What is the probability that you will choose a letter in the first half of the alphabet (A–M)?

4. What is the probability that you will choose one of the last five letters in the alphabet?

L. Task: Adding and Subtracting Fractions (URG p. 16)

A. $\frac{3}{6} + \frac{2}{6} =$ B. $\frac{2}{3} + \frac{1}{5} =$

C. $\frac{1}{4} - \frac{1}{6} =$ D. $\frac{5}{8} - \frac{1}{4} =$

E. $\frac{3}{8} - \frac{1}{8} =$ F. $\frac{1}{2} - \frac{2}{5} =$

N. Challenge: A Busy School Day!
(URG p. 17)

1. On an average school day, Jackie spends six hours in school. What percent of her day is spent in school?

2. Jackie practices piano one hour on a school day. What fraction of the day does she spend practicing piano?

3. Jackie spends $\frac{1}{3}$ of a day sleeping. How many hours does she sleep?

4. What fraction of Jackie's day is left after school, piano, and sleep? More or less than $\frac{1}{2}$ of a day?

5. Write a similar story using your own daily activities.

Suggestions for Teaching the Lesson (continued)

Assessment

To grade the lab, assign a given number of points to each part of the lab and grade each part based on the following criteria:

1. Drawing the picture
   - Is the procedure clearly illustrated?
   - Are the variables labeled?

2. Collecting and recording the data
   - Are the intervals in the first column correct? (They should all be the same size and the intervals should not overlap.)
   - Are the correct units of measure (seconds) included?
   - Does the sum of the number of bubbles in the third column equal the number of bubbles in the sample?
   - Are the percents correct?

3. Graphing the data
   - Does the graph have a title?
   - Are the axes scaled correctly and labeled clearly?
   - Does the scale on the horizontal axis match the intervals in the first column of the data table?
   - Are the bars drawn correctly?

4. Solving the problems
   - Are the answers correct based on the data?
   - Are the answers, including the explanations, clear and complete?

Score student responses to *Questions 10–12* using the Telling dimension of the *TIMS Multidimensional Rubric*. To help you use the rubric to score students' work, consider the following questions:

- Did students clearly describe the shapes of their graphs?

- Did students connect the shapes of the graphs to the data? Did they explain how the heights of the bars reflect the life spans of the bubbles?

- Did students compare their graphs to their predictions in *Question 6?* Did they tell why their predictions were correct or incorrect?

- Did they compare their graphs to the graphs of the American robin, oysters, and humans? Did each student explain why the shape of his or her graph is like the shape of one of these three graphs? Are the shapes of the graphs connected to the life spans of the animals and soap bubbles?

Extensions

- In a class discussion, compare the graphs from each group with one another. Are most of the graphs similar to one another? Why or why not? If all the groups used the same bubble solution and followed the same procedures, all the graphs should look similar to one another.

- After you have compared the groups' graphs with one another, combine the data from all of the groups and make a graph which shows the percent of bubbles that live for any given length of time. Compare the class graph with the groups' graphs. How are they alike? How are they different? Since the class graph and the groups' graphs show the percent of bubbles, the class graph should look similar to the groups' graphs.

- Compare the graphs from this lab with the graphs from Lesson 5 *Life Spans*. How do the two graphs for Lesson 5 compare with the graph for the bubbles?

Software Connection

Students can make graphs similar to those they made in class using *Graph Master* or a similar graphing and data analysis program. They enter the number of seconds each bubble "lived" in one column of the data table. Students then use the tally function before asking for a graph. If students choose histogram as the type of graph, the program will ask for the size of the intervals for the horizontal axis. Choosing the interval size will bin the data. Note that the graphs will have the same shape as those the students made in class. However, the variable on the vertical axis will be frequency, or number of bubbles, instead of percent of bubbles.

AT A GLANCE

Math Facts and Daily Practice and Problems

Complete DPP items I–N. Items I, K, and M review math facts. Items J, L, and N review concepts on the midyear test in Lesson 8.

Part 1. Launching the Investigation

1. Discuss the descriptions of the lives of different kinds of animals in the *Comparing Lives of Animals and Soap Bubbles* Lab Pages in the *Student Guide*. Match the descriptions with the graphs in *Question 1*.
2. Students observe a few bubbles. Use *Questions 2–3* to identify the variables and develop the procedure for the lab.

Part 2. Drawing the Picture and Collecting the Data

1. Students draw a picture of the procedures and label the variables. *(Question 4)*
2. Before collecting data, students time a few bubbles and use this information to choose intervals to bin the data and to predict the shape of the graph. *(Questions 5–6)*
3. Students fill in the first column of the data table with appropriate intervals. *(Question 7)*
4. Students collect the data and complete the data table. *(Question 8)*

Part 3. Graphing the Data

Students make a bar graph of the data. They will need graph paper. *(Question 9)*

Part 4. Analyzing the Data

Review the Student Rubric: *Telling*. Have students use the rubric to guide them in writing their responses to *Questions 10–12*.

Homework

1. Assign some or all of the review problems in Lesson 7 for homework.
2. Assign Parts 3 and 4 of the Home Practice.

Assessment

1. Grade the lab by assigning points to drawing the picture, collecting and recording the data, graphing, and solving problems.
2. Score student responses to *Questions 10–12* using the Telling dimension of the *TIMS Multidimensional Rubric*.

Notes:

Student Guide

Questions 1–12 (SG pp. 277–279)

1. A. *robins
   B. *humans
   C. *oysters

2. *Time at which the bubbles pop and percent of bubbles that pop after any given number of seconds. Other variables which affect the life span of a bubble: Type of bubble solution, whether the bubble is held on a wand or allowed to drop to the ground, ventilation in the room, air temperature, humidity, and size of bubble.

3. *See Lesson Guide 6 for a description of possible procedures.

4. *See Figure 11 in Lesson Guide 6 for a sample picture.

5. *Yes, intervals will vary.

6. Descriptions and sketches will vary.

7.*–8.* See Figure 12 in Lesson Guide 6 for a sample data table.

9. *See Figure 13 in Lesson Guide 6 for a sample graph.

10. *For the sample graph in Figure 13, all the bars lie between 30 and 70 seconds and three of the four bars are similar in height. The bubbles all lived for a long time and all burst after about the same amount of time.

11. Answers will vary.

12. *Answers will vary. This graph is similar to the graph for humans in Figure 13 in Lesson Guide 6.

Discovery Assignment Book

**Home Practice (DAB p. 128)

Part 3. Review of Fractions

Questions 1–3

1. A. $\frac{13}{8}$ or $1\frac{5}{8}$
   B. $\frac{3}{6}$ or $\frac{1}{2}$
   C. $\frac{8}{12}$ or $\frac{2}{3}$

2. A. $\frac{22}{3}$
   B. $\frac{17}{5}$
   C. $\frac{89}{8}$

3. A. $4\frac{2}{3}$
   B. $9\frac{2}{7}$
   C. $10\frac{3}{10}$

Part 4. Geometry Review

Questions 1–4

1. 29 sq cm

2. 90°

3. 135°

4. The area of the rectangle is 25.3 sq cm which means it has less area than the shape in Question 1. (5.5 cm × 4.6 cm = 25.3 sq cm)

Soap Bubbles Data Table (DAB p. 143)

*See Figure 12 in Lesson Guide 6 for a sample data table.

---

*Answers and/or discussion are included in the Lesson Guide.

**Answers for all the Home Practice in the *Discovery Assignment Book* are at the end of the unit.

OPTIONAL LESSON

There are no Daily Practice and Problems items for this lesson.

LESSON GUIDE 7

Review Problems

Estimated Class Sessions: 1

Students solve a variety of multistep word problems that review concepts and skills from the first seven units. They make choices about the tools they use to solve the problems.

Key Content

- Solving multistep word problems.
- Communicating solutions orally and in writing.
- Choosing appropriate methods and tools to calculate (calculator, ruler, or small centiwheels).
- Choosing to find an estimate or an exact answer.
- Representing decimals using circle graphs (centiwheels).
- Drawing and interpreting best-fit lines.
- Using graphs and fractions to express ratios.
- Finding equal ratios.

Key Vocabulary

compost

Materials List

Print Materials for Students

		Optional Activity	Homework
Student Books	**Student Guide**	*Review Problems* Pages 280–281	
	Discovery Assignment Book		Home Practice Part 6 Page 130
Teacher Resources	**Generic Section** ⊙	*Centimeter Graph Paper,* 1 per student	

⊙ *available on Teacher Resource CD*

All Transparency Masters, Blackline Masters, and Assessment Blackline Masters in the Unit Resource Guide are on the Teacher Resource CD.

Supplies for Each Student

calculator
centiwheel
ruler

Developing the Activity

This problem set can serve several purposes. It presents opportunities for students to practice choosing appropriate methods for solving problems. It also provides practice with a variety of problem types and math concepts. For some problems an exact answer is necessary. For others, an estimate is appropriate.

Use this problem set as a review for the *Midyear Test*. Students can work in groups to discuss strategies to solve each problem. (Note that students may be unfamiliar with the word **compost** in *Question 8*. Define compost for them.) You can also use the problems to augment students' homework for the unit. Alternatively, you may choose to use some of the problems as an assessment.

Review Problems

Answer the following questions. You may use any tools that you use in class. For example, you may need to use a ruler, a calculator, or a small centiwheel. You will need graph paper to complete Question 6. Show all your work.

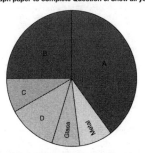

Lin, Irma, Romesh, and John presented this circle graph to their class during a unit on the environment. This graph shows one way experts divide the categories of trash thrown into landfills.

Use this graph to answer Questions 1–5.

1. Organic waste makes up 25% of our trash. What part of the circle graph represents organic waste?

2. We throw away about the same amount of plastic as we do metal. What part of the circle graph represents plastic?

3. Paper makes up between one-third and one-half of our garbage. What part of the circle graph represents paper?

4. There are some things that we throw away that do not fit any of the categories we have listed so far. Examples might include an old telephone or a worn-out chair. This category is labeled miscellaneous. About $\frac{1}{8}$ the garbage we throw out is considered miscellaneous. What part of the circle graph represents the category miscellaneous?

Student Guide - Page 280

---

5. About what percent of our trash comes from each category? Use a small centiwheel to help you.

6. Brandon and Roberto discovered an interesting fact while studying recycling: The energy saved from recycling one glass bottle will light a 100-watt bulb for four hours.

   A. Use this fact to complete the data table below. Copy the completed data table on your paper.

N Number of Recycled Glass Bottles	t Time (in hours) a 100-Watt Bulb Can Burn
1	4
3	
	20
7	

   B. Make a graph using your data table.
   C. Use your graph to find how many hours you can light a 100-watt bulb from the energy saved from 4 recycled glass bottles. Show your work on your graph.
   D. If you recycled 10 glass bottles, how many hours can a 100-watt bulb burn with the energy saved? Show your work.
   E. Write a ratio of time to number of glass bottles as a fraction.
   F. Write 2 ratios equivalent to the ratio in Question 6E.

7. Today, about $\frac{1}{5}$ of our paper is recycled. About what percent of our paper is recycled?

8. Alexis, Felicia, and Ana found that you can compost most organic waste. They learned that 1 pound of red worms will eat 0.5 pounds of organic waste each day. The students in Mr. Moreno's class built a worm bin to compost the organic waste from their lunches. The students produce an average of 3.25 pounds of organic waste each week. How many pounds of red worms will they need in their bin if they expect the waste to be fully composted weekly?

Student Guide - Page 281

Part 6 A Birthday Party

Solve the following problems. Choose an appropriate method for each:
mental math, paper and pencil, or a calculator. Explain your solutions.
Use a separate sheet of paper to show your work.

1. Today is Manny's birthday. He invited 19 of his friends to a pizza party at
   Cheesy Weesy Pizza. Each child will eat 3 slices of pizza. How many slices
   of pizza will they need? (Don't forget Manny.)

2. The menu reads as follows: Large Pizza (16 slices) $14.00; Medium Pizza
   (12 slices) $10.50; Small Pizza (8 slices) $8.00. List three possible orders
   that will feed the 20 children. Which of the three orders is the cheapest?

3. One-half of the children want cheese and sausage pizza. One-fourth want
   cheese pizza. One-fourth want pepperoni pizza.
   A. How many children want cheese and sausage?
   B. How many want cheese?
   C. How many children want pepperoni?

4. One-half of the children at the party drank two glasses of soda each. The
   rest drank 1 glass each.
   A. How many total glasses of soda did they drink?
   B. Manny's parents ordered pitchers of soda. If each pitcher of soda serves
      5 glasses, how many pitchers were ordered?
   C. If one pitcher costs $1.75, what was the total cost for all of the pitchers
      of soda?

5. What was the total cost of the party? (Include the cheapest cost of the
   pizzas and the soda.)

6. Manny's grandfather gave Manny a $100 bill. Manny uses this money to pay
   for the party. He plans on putting the rest into his savings account. How
   much will Manny have left for his savings account?

Copyright © Kendall/Hunt Publishing Company

130 DAB · Grade 5 · Unit 8   APPLICATIONS: AN ASSESSMENT UNIT

Discovery Assignment Book - Page 130

Suggestions for Teaching the Lesson

Homework and Practice

- Assign some or all of the problems for homework.

- Assign Part 6 of the Home Practice which
  includes multistep word problems.

*Answers for Part 6 of the Home Practice can be found in
the Answer Key at the end of this lesson and at the end of
this unit.*

Resources

- Appelhoff, Mary, Mary Frances Fenton, and
  Barbara Loss Harris. *Worms Eat Our Garbage.*
  Flower Press, Kalamazoo, MI, 1993.

- The EarthWorks Group. *50 Simple Things Kids
  Can Do to Save the Earth.* Andrews and
  McMeel, Kansas City, MO, 1999.

AT A GLANCE

Developing the Activity

Students solve *Questions 1–8* on the *Review Problems* Activity Pages in the *Student Guide*
using calculators, centiwheels, and rulers.

Homework

1. Assign some or all of the problems for review, homework, or assessment.
2. Assign Part 6 of the Home Practice.

Notes:

Student Guide

Questions 1–8 (SG pp. 280–281)

1. purple—B
2. green—C
3. red—A
4. orange—D
5. Part A: About 40%

   Part B: 25%

   Part C: About 8%

   Part D: About 12%

   Glass: About 7%

   Metal: About 8%

6. **A.**

N Number of Recycled Glass Bottles	t Time (in Hours) a 100-Watt Bulb Can Burn
1	4
3	12
5	20
7	28

B.

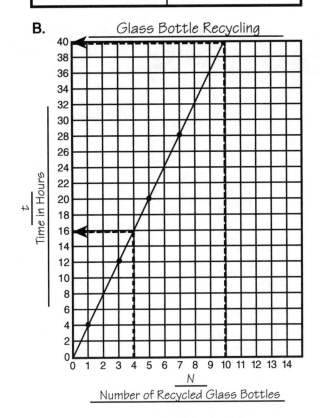

C. 16 hours

D. 40 hours

E. Ratios will vary. One possible ratio is $\frac{4 \text{ hours}}{1 \text{ bottle}}$.

F. Ratios will vary. Two possible ratios are: $\frac{8 \text{ hours}}{2 \text{ bottles}}$ and $\frac{12 \text{ hours}}{3 \text{ bottles}}$.

7. 20%

8. About 6.5 pounds

Discovery Assignment Book

**Home Practice (DAB p. 130)

Part 6. A Birthday Party

Questions 1–6

1. 60 slices of pizza

2. Answers will vary. Here are some possible combinations and their total cost:

   3 medium and 3 small pizzas ($55.50)

   3 medium, 1 small, and 1 large pizza ($53.50)

   2 large, 2 small, and 1 medium pizza ($54.50)

   5 medium pizzas ($52.50)

   3 large and 1 medium pizza ($52.50)

   4 large pizzas ($56.00)

3. **A.** 10 children want cheese and sausage

   B. 5 children want cheese

   C. 5 children want pepperoni

4. **A.** 30 glasses

   B. 6 pitchers

   C. $10.50

5. Answers will vary depending on the cheapest order the child finds for *Question 2.* If the total cost for pizza was $52.50 and the total cost of soda was $10.50, then the total cost of the party was $63.00.

6. Answers will vary. Based on the answer in *Question 5:* $37.00

---

*Answers and/or discussion are included in the Lesson Guide.

**Answers for all the Home Practice in the *Discovery Assignment Book* are at the end of the unit.

Daily Practice and Problems:
Bit for Lesson 8

O. Estimating with Money (URG p. 17) $ N

Estimate the answers to the following problems.

A. $34.56 + $72.35

B. $0.39 + $1.76

C. $0.58 × 8

D. $275.34 − $56.23

Explain your strategy for B.

DPP Challenge is on page 85. Suggestions for using the DPPs are on page 85.

LESSON GUIDE 8

Midyear Test

Estimated Class Sessions: 1–2

Students complete a paper-and-pencil test consisting of 14 items. Students will use a calculator, a protractor, and a ruler to complete some items on this test. Items on this test are from Units 1–8.

Key Content

* Assessing skills and concepts from the first seven units.

Materials List

Print Materials for Students

		Math Facts and Daily Practice and Problems	Assessment Activity	Written Assessment
Teacher Resources	**Unit Resource Guide**	DPP Items O–P Pages 17–18 ⊙		*Midyear Test* Pages 87–91, 1 per student ⊙
	Generic Section ⊙		*Centimeter Dot Paper,* 1 per student (optional)	

⊙ *available on Teacher Resource CD*

All Transparency Masters, Blackline Masters, and Assessment Blackline Masters in the Unit Resource Guide are on the Teacher Resource CD.

Supplies for Each Student

calculator
ruler
protractor

Developing the Activity

Students take this test independently. It is designed to take one class period. You may make adjustments as needed. The first three items of this test (Part One) are to be completed without a calculator. After students complete this part of the test, they may begin Part 2. Students will need a ruler, a protractor, and a calculator to complete Part 2. *Centimeter Dot Paper* should be available, as students may choose to use this to complete **Question 9.**

Remind students to be clear and concise when describing their problem-solving strategies.

Look over the problems before administering the test. If you have not covered the skills required to complete a question, omit the question from the test.

Suggestions for Teaching the Lesson

Math Facts

Remind students to study the multiplication and division facts at home in order to prepare for the Inventory Test in DPP item Q in the next lesson.

Extension

Assign DPP Challenge P to students who complete the test early. Item P presents number puzzles that involve decimals.

Daily Practice and Problems:
Challenge for Lesson 8

P. Challenge: Number Puzzles
(URG p. 18)

A. I am 3 tenths less than 5 times 7. Who am I?

B. I am twice the sum of 3.4 and 2.1. Who am I?

C. I am less than 10 but more than 5. If you skip count by two-tenths (.2) starting at 0 you get me. The digit in the ones' place is the same as the digit in the tenths' place. My ones' digit is a multiple of 4.

AT A GLANCE

Math Facts and Daily Practice and Problems

1. Complete DPP items O–P. Bit O involves estimating with money. Challenge P provides number puzzles.
2. Remind students to study for the *Multiplication and Division Fact Inventory Test.*

Developing the Activity

1. Students solve the first three problems without a calculator.
2. Students complete Part 2 of the test using a ruler, a protractor, and a calculator. Students may also use *Centimeter Dot Paper.*

Notes:

Name _____ Date _____

Midyear Test

Solve the following problems without using your calculator.

1. There are 5 children in a group. The children have 3275 marbles to share equally. How many marbles will each child get? Show your work.

2. **A.** 694
        $\times 8$

    B. 83
        $\times 27$

    C. 2.2
        $\times 0.49$

    D. $7\overline{)2417}$

3. Estimate the answers to the following problems.

    A. 697,000 × 20

    B. 215,000 ÷ 70

Name _____ Date _____

To answer the questions in Part Two, you may use any of the tools you use in class. You will need a ruler, a protractor, and a calculator. You may also use *Centimeter Dot Paper.*

4. Write the following number in words.

   3,547,899

5. Find the area of the figure.
   Explain your strategies.
   Give your answer in centimeters.

   Area =

   Strategies:

6. Complete the table. Write the following fractions as decimals and percents.

Fraction	Decimal	Percent (to the nearest percent)
$\frac{51}{100}$		
$\frac{6}{10}$		
$\frac{3}{50}$		
$\frac{956}{1000}$		

7. John wrote the problem: $1.5 + 2.15 = 2.30$. Nicholas thought John had done the problem wrong. How can Nicholas explain John's mistake?

Name _____   Date _____

8. The students at Bessie Coleman Elementary School started a paper recycling project. Each week, the students collect the used paper from each classroom. They weigh the paper and then take it to a recycling center. The students made a graph showing the total amount of paper they recycled so far. Use the graph to answer the following questions.

Paper Recycling

N — Total Number of Pounds Recycled

t — Time in Weeks

A. Draw a best-fit line.

B. Choose a point on the line and use it to write a fraction to show the ratio of the number of pounds of paper recycled to time in weeks.

C. For every 117 pounds of paper students recycle, they can save an average-size tree. About how many weeks will students have to recycle to save one tree?

D. If there are 36 weeks in the school year, about how many trees can the students save in one school year?

9. Solve the following problems. Show your work.

A. $\frac{3}{8} + \frac{1}{4} =$ **B.** $\frac{7}{10} - \frac{1}{2} =$

10. Use the symbols <, >, and = to compare these fractions.

A. $\frac{3}{4}, \frac{9}{12}$ **B.** $\frac{1}{2}, \frac{3}{8}$

C. $\frac{8}{9}, \frac{7}{9}$ **D.** $\frac{1}{5}, \frac{1}{3}$

11. Change these mixed numbers to improper fractions.

A. $1\frac{7}{8}$ **B.** $6\frac{4}{9}$

Name _____   Date _____

12. Change these fractions to mixed numbers.

   A. $\frac{11}{7}$ B. $\frac{23}{5}$

13. Find the sum of the interior angles of this figure. Use any method you wish. Explain your work.

14. Use these measurements to draw quadrilateral ABCD: side AB = 4 cm; angle A = 90 degrees; side DA = 4.7 cm; angle B = 90 degrees; and side BC = 2.5 cm.

   A. What is the length of side DC?

   B. What is the measure of angle C?

Unit Resource Guide

Midyear Test (URG pp. 87–91)

Questions 1–14

1. 655 marbles

2. **A.** 5552

   B. 2241

   C. 1.078

   D. 345 R2

3. **A.** Estimates will vary. One possible solution is: $700,000 \times 20 = 14,000,000$.

   B. Estimates will vary. One possible estimate is: $210,000 \div 70 = 3000$.

4. Three million, five hundred forty-seven thousand, eight hundred ninety-nine

5. 12.5 square centimeters; Strategies will vary. Students might measure the length and the width and multiply or they might draw a centimeter grid and count the area.

6. Decimals: 0.51, 0.6, 0.06, 0.956

   Percents: 51%, 60%, 6%, 96%

7. Answers will vary. John added incorrect place values. He added five-tenths to 5 hundredths and one to 1 tenth. By estimating the solution, Nicholas could say that the answer must be bigger than 3 ($2 + 1 = 3$ and $2.15 + 1.5$ must be bigger than 3). The correct answer is 3.65.

8.

A. Ratios will vary. One possible ratio is $\frac{120 \text{ pounds}}{3 \text{ weeks}}$.

B. About 3 weeks

C. About 12 trees

9. Strategies may vary.

   A. $\frac{5}{8}$

   B. $\frac{2}{10}$ or $\frac{1}{5}$

10. **A.** $\frac{3}{4} = \frac{9}{12}$

    B. $\frac{1}{2} > \frac{3}{8}$

    C. $\frac{8}{9} > \frac{7}{9}$

    D. $\frac{1}{5} < \frac{1}{3}$

11. **A.** $\frac{15}{8}$

    B. $\frac{58}{9}$

*Answers and/or discussion are included in the Lesson Guide.

**Answers for all the Home Practice in the *Discovery Assignment Book* are at the end of the unit.

12. **A.** $1\frac{4}{7}$

   B. $4\frac{3}{5}$

13. 540°; Explanations will vary. Students may triangulate the pentagon or they may use a protractor.

14.
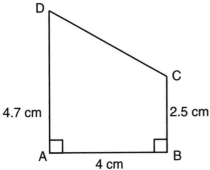

   A. About 4.5 cm

   B. 120°

*Answers and/or discussion are included in the Lesson Guide.
**Answers for all the Home Practice in the *Discovery Assignment Book* are at the end of the unit.

URG • Grade 5 • Unit 8 • Lesson 8 • Answer Key   93

Q. *Multiplication and Division Fact Inventory Test* (URG p. 18)

Students take a test that contains the facts from all five groups of facts studied in Units 2–8—the 5s and 10s, 2s and 3s, square numbers, 9s, and the last six facts.

Students should have two pens or pencils of different colors ready. During the first four minutes of the test, students write their answers using one color pen or pencil. Encourage students first to answer all the facts they know well and can answer quickly. Then, they should go back and use strategies to solve the rest. After four minutes have passed, give students more time to complete the remaining items with the other color pen or pencil.

Using the results of the test, students should update their new *Multiplication* and *Division Facts I Know* charts.

DPP Task is on page 97. Suggestions for using the DPPs are on page 97.

LESSON GUIDE 9
Portfolio Review

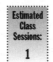

Estimated Class Sessions: 1

Students review the work they have collected so far this year to decide which pieces to include in their portfolios.

Key Content

- Using portfolios.
- Reflecting on one's own work.

Curriculum Sequence

Before This Unit

In Unit 1 students placed completed activities and labs in collection folders in anticipation of choosing work to include in a more formal portfolio. In Unit 2 Lesson 10 students were encouraged to begin a portfolio by choosing pieces from their collection folders. They started a Table of Contents for their portfolios as well. Students added work to their collection folders throughout the first seven units. Periodically they chose work from their collection folders to add to their portfolios.

After This Unit

Students will continue to save work in their collection folders as the year progresses. They will review their collection folders periodically and choose pieces for inclusion in student portfolios. Work in the portfolios will show growth over time.

Materials List

Print Materials for Students

	Math Facts and Daily Practice and Problems	Assessment Activity	Written Assessment
Student Book — Student Guide		*Portfolio Review* Pages 282–283	
Teacher Resources — Facts Resource Guide	DPP Item 8Q		
Teacher Resources — Unit Resource Guide	DPP Items Q–R Pages 18–20		DPP Item Q, *Multiplication and Division Fact Inventory Test* Page 20, 1 per student

available on Teacher Resource CD

All Transparency Masters, Blackline Masters, and Assessment Blackline Masters in the Unit Resource Guide are on the Teacher Resource CD.

Supplies for Each Student

portfolio folder
collection folder

Developing the Activity

This is a good time for students again to review, organize, and add to their portfolios. There are many ways to accomplish this. Specific suggestions for students are on the *Portfolio Review* Assessment Pages in the *Student Guide.* You may follow these suggestions, or you may choose other activities for your students. See the TIMS Tutor: *Portfolios* in the *Teacher Implementation Guide.*

TIMS Tip

The Lesson Guide for Unit 2 Lesson 10 suggested that students focus their portfolios on a specific area such as measurement, graphing, or communication. If you choose a focus for the portfolios, review this with your students before choosing pieces to add to their portfolios.

The assessment tasks from previous units and the tasks in this unit make good entries in portfolios. Including these tasks in the students' portfolios will allow you, your students, and their parents to assess growth in mathematics learning over time. For example, student performance on the lab *Distance vs. Time* (Unit 3) can be compared to student performance on *A Day at the Races* (Unit 5). Similarly, a student can compare his or her work on the lab *Searching the Forest* (Unit 1) to work on *Comparing Lives of Animals and Soap Bubbles* (Unit 8). By reviewing these labs, improvement in students' abilities to collect, organize, and graph data will be evident. In the same way, look for growth in students' abilities to communicate solutions to problems by comparing student work on earlier assessment tasks to work on *Florence Kelley's Report.* Similar tasks include *Stack Up* from Unit 2 and *Making Shapes* from Unit 6. The *Multiplication and Division Fact Inventory Test* or *Facts I Know* charts are also appropriate entries.

Portfolio Review

Since the start of the school year, the students in Mr. Moreno's class have collected work for their portfolios. They have saved work that shows what they know, how they solve problems, and how well they can explain their work. Today, the students are updating their portfolios.

"Look through the work in your collection folders," said Mr. Moreno. "Find the activities and labs that best show how you use what you know to solve problems. These are the pieces that you should put in your portfolio. You can compare the work you did earlier this year to the work you are doing now. And don't forget to update your table of contents."

1. If you have not done so recently, choose items from your collection folder to add to your portfolio. Examples of items you might choose are:
   • *Distance vs. Time* from Unit 3
   • *A Day at the Races* from Unit 5
   • *Making Shapes* from Unit 6
   • Work with paper-and-pencil multiplication and division

2. Put your *Experiment Review Chart* from Lesson 1 in your portfolio.

Student Guide - Page 282

---

3. Choose one or two other pieces of work from this unit to include in your portfolio. Select pieces that are like other work that you put in your portfolio earlier in the year. For example, if you already have a lab in your portfolio, put *Comparing Lives of Animals and Soap Bubbles* in your portfolio too. Or, if you included a written solution to a problem like *Stack Up,* then also include your writing and graph for *Florence Kelley's Report* in Lesson 4.

4. Add to your Table of Contents. The Table of Contents should include the name of each piece of work, a short description of the work, and the date it was finished.

5. Write a paragraph comparing two pieces of work in your portfolio that are alike in some way. For example, you can compare two labs or your solutions to two problems you have solved. One piece should be new and one should be from earlier in the year. Here are some questions for you to think about as you write your paragraph:
   • Which two pieces did you choose to compare?
   • How are they alike? How are they different?
   • Do you see any improvement in the newest piece of work as compared to the older work? Explain.
   • If you could redo the older piece of work, how would you improve it?
   • How could you improve the newer piece of work?

6. Write about your favorite piece of work in your portfolio. Tell why you like it. Explain what you learned from it.

My favorite piece is my work on *Florence Kelley.*

When I compare my work on *Stack Up* to my work on the slab maker problems, I can really see a difference.

Student Guide - Page 283

Besides the completed *Experiment Review Chart* from Lesson 1, you may choose at least one more item from this unit that all students will include in their portfolios, then let each student choose one other piece to include. They should place their work in chronological order and update the table of contents. Every two to three weeks, remind students to review the contents of their collection folders and portfolios and choose one or two new pieces to include in their portfolios.

 TIMS Tip

Keep the number of items in a portfolio manageable. Ten to twelve well-chosen and chronologically arranged pieces per semester may be most useful. To be able to document growth in mathematical learning over time, include similar items from the beginning, middle, and end of the year. Vary the types of assessments.

One way to encourage student reflection is for them to write about the work in their portfolios. *Question 5* in the *Student Guide* asks students to compare two pieces of work in their portfolios. *Question 6* asks each student to write about his or her favorite piece of work. Students' written responses to these questions can be attached to the appropriate labs or activities.

Suggestions for Teaching the Lesson

Math Facts

DPP item Q assesses the multiplication and division facts with a short paper-and-pencil test.

Homework and Practice

Assign DPP item R as practice in reading and interpreting line graphs.

Daily Practice and Problems: Task for Lesson 9

R. Task: Currency (URG p. 19)

The currency in the European Union is called a Euro. In 2002, 1 Euro was worth 90 cents in the United States. Make a graph to show the number of Euros and their value in the U.S. Graph Number of Euros on the horizontal axis and Value in U.S. Dollars and Cents on the vertical axis.

1. How much were 30 Euros worth in U.S. money?

2. If you trade $30.00 of U.S. money for Euros, about how many Euros will you receive?

AT A GLANCE

Math Facts and Daily Practice and Problems

Complete DPP items Q–R. Item Q assesses the multiplication and division facts using an inventory test that follows DPP item R.

Developing the Activity

1. Students review their work in their collection folders and portfolios.
2. Using suggestions on the *Portfolio Review* Activity Pages in the *Student Guide,* students choose activities and labs to include in their portfolios. Other than the *Experiment Review Chart* which was completed in Lesson 1 of this unit, choose one other piece of work from this unit for all students to include. Have students choose a third item themselves.
3. Students update the table of contents.
4. Students write about the work in their portfolios. See *Questions 5–6* in the *Student Guide.*

Homework

DPP item R can be assigned as homework.

Notes:

Student Guide

Questions 1–6 (SG pp. 282–283)

Answers will vary.

*Answers and/or discussion are included in the Lesson Guide.

**Answers for all the Home Practice in the *Discovery Assignment Book* are at the end of the unit.

URG • Grade 5 • Unit 8 • Lesson 9 • Answer Key 99

Discovery Assignment Book

Part 2. Practicing the Operations

Questions 1–2 (DAB p. 127)

1. **A.** 4392   **B.** 8.03

    C. 543 R3   **D.** 17.69

2. Answers will vary. Possible strategies are shown.

    A. $80,000 \div 40 = 2000$

    B. $100,000 \div 25 = 4000$

    C. $10,000 \times 14 = 140,000$

    D. $200 \times 300,000 = 60,000,000$

Part 3. Review of Fractions

Questions 1–3 (DAB p. 128)

1. **A.** $\frac{13}{8}$ or $1\frac{5}{8}$

    B. $\frac{3}{6}$ or $\frac{1}{2}$

    C. $\frac{8}{12}$ or $\frac{2}{3}$

2. **A.** $\frac{22}{3}$

    B. $\frac{17}{5}$

    C. $\frac{89}{8}$

3. **A.** $4\frac{2}{3}$

    B. $9\frac{2}{7}$

    C. $10\frac{3}{10}$

Part 4. Geometry Review

Questions 1–4 (DAB p. 128)

1. 29 sq cm

2. 90°

3. 135°

4. The area of the rectangle is 25.3 sq cm which means it has less area than the shape in **Question 1.** (5.5 cm × 4.6 cm = 25.3 sq cm)

Part 5. How Long Are Names?

Questions 1–4 (DAB p. 129)

1. Answers will vary. The graph on the left can be titled "Number of Letters in First Names" and

the graph on the right can be titled "Number of Letters in First and Last Names."

2. Answers will vary. Some students may mention that for the data in the graph on the left there is a larger range for the number of letters (10–16 letters) but shorter bars. The graph on the right has a smaller range for the number of letters (4–7) but more data for the numbers within that range (taller bars).

3. Answers will vary. Students will probably mention that the data for the graph on the left shows a larger number of letters in names than the graph on the right and is therefore the graph showing the letters for first and last names combined.

4. Answers will vary. Possible response: The bars on the graph will be between 3 and 8 letters. The bars will be about twice as tall as the bars on the graph for one class.

Part 6. A Birthday Party

Questions 1–6 (DAB p. 130)

1. 60 slices of pizza

2. Answers will vary. Here are some possible combinations and their total cost:

    3 medium and 3 small pizzas ($55.50)

    3 medium, 1 small, and 1 large pizza ($53.50)

    2 large, 2 small, and 1 medium pizza ($54.50)

    5 medium pizzas ($52.50)

    3 large and 1 medium pizza ($52.50)

    4 large pizzas ($56.00)

3. **A.** 10 children want cheese and sausage

    B. 5 children want cheese

    C. 5 children want pepperoni

4. **A.** 30 glasses

    B. 6 pitchers

    C. $10.50

5. Answers will vary depending on the cheapest order the child finds for **Question 2.** If the total cost for pizza was $52.50 and the total cost of soda was $10.50, then the total cost of the party was $63.00.

6. Answers will vary. Based on the answer in **Question 5:** $37.00

*Answers and/or discussion are included in the Lesson Guide.